OTHER TITLES IN THE SERIES ON ANALYTICAL CHEMISTRY

INTERNATIONAL SERIES OF M

ANALYTICAL CHEMISTR

GENERAL EDITORS: R. BELCHER AND L.

Volume 8

ORGANIC FUNCTIONAL
GROUP ANALYSIS

ORGANIC FUNCTIONAL GROUP ANALYSIS

by

F. E. CRITCHFIELD

Research and Development Dept.,
Union Carbide Chemicals Co.,
South Charlestown 3, West Virginia, U.S.A.

A Pergamon Press Book

THE MACMILLAN COMPANY

NEW YORK

1963

CONTENTS

v

PREFA[CE]

THE purpose of this book is to pro[vide]
a collection of versatile and reliable
mining most of the more common or[ganic]
attempt has been made to present the m[ethods]
required to solve the maximum numb[er]
and known limitations of each meth[od]
the analytical chemist can decide wh[ich]
consideration can be applied to his
actual procedures are written in such
be followed by competent non-technic[al]
all of the methods discussed are in rou[tine]
laboratories of Union Carbide Chemical[s]
grateful to this company for their coope[ration]
I am also grateful to J. B. Johnson and
helpful suggestions and excellent methods
to the field. Many other analytical chemis[ts]
have either contributed original procedure[s]
fications that are presented. Where possible,
are referenced. I am also indebted to R. S. [C]
editing the manuscript.

F. E.

1 Organic Functional

CHAPTER 1

INTRODUCTION

NEW techniques of organic analysis are being developed at a rate that is at least equivalent to the rate of expansion of the field of organic chemistry itself. One reason for this is the major role analytical chemistry plays in the rapidly expanding organic chemical industry.

This book is devoted to one aspect of organic analysis that is sometimes overlooked for the more glamorous instrumental techniques that are appearing upon the analytical scene. Chemical methods involve the determination of organic compounds via reactions of their functional groups and are usually simple, accurate, and precise means of analysis. This is not meant to imply that such chemical methods are analytical panaceas, because there are many analyses that can not be performed in this manner. In particular, chemical methods are of little value for analyzing hydrocarbons, ethers, and mixtures of compounds of the same homologous series. Such analyses can be more readily performed by instrumental methods, such as gas chromatography.

Chemical methods are particularly valuable for (1) the determination of the purity of refined materials; (2) the determination of ppm concentrations of organic compounds; (3) the analysis of research samples; (4) the calibration of instrumental methods; and (5) the rapid analysis of process samples.

This book contains a discussion of chemical methods recommended for determination of most of the more common organic functional groups. The principle, procedure, and scope and limitations of each method is discussed in detail. Practically all of the methods have been used routinely in the various laboratories of Union Carbide Chemicals Company and several of them have never been published heretofore.

1*

No attempt has been made to provide a literature survey of methods for determining each functional group; however, references pertinent to the methods discussed are given. The particular methods selected for presentation in this book were selected mainly on the basis of general applicability, accuracy, reproducibility, and simplicity. A few methods of fairly limited applicability are discussed; however, in most of these cases the methods are presented because of their specificity. Some excellent chemical methods for organic functional groups may have been omitted; however, an attempt has been made to include those that fulfil the requirements specified above.

TECHNIQUES

The techniques used in performing the methods discussed in this book are simple, and usually special equipment is not required for the analysis. The methods are either titrimetric or colorimetric in nature. The titrimetric methods are of most value for determining macro concentrations of organic compounds, while the colorimetric methods are recommended for determinations in the ppm range. Indicators are specified for selecting the end point of practically all titrations; however, in a few cases potentiometric titrations may be desirable and this will require the use of conventional pH meters. The colorimetric methods, of course, require a visible spectrophotometer.

Most of the reactions are conducted at room temperature or at the temperature of boiling water. In the latter case, the reactions are conducted in heat-resistant pressure bottles, enclosed in fabric bags, and immersed in a steam bath.

The use of pressure bottles for conducting reactions at elevated temperatures is very convenient and less subject to atmospheric contamination than reflux techniques. Some investigators may have misgivings about this application; however, the use of the bottles under the conditions specified is a safe operation. The particular bottles used in the author's laboratory* have been

* One source of supply for suitable bottles is B. Preiser Company Inc., Charleston, West Virginia. A source of supply for the fabric bags is Flaherty-Kennedy Filter Fabrics, Maplewood, New Jersey.

thoroughly safety tested at Union Carbide and no failures have been observed at pressures below 120 psig. Most of the bottles are capable of withstanding pressures up to 450 psig. Under the reaction conditions specified in the methods in this book, pressures higher than approximately 50 psig are not encountered.

CHAPTER 2

ACIDS AND BASES

A KNOWLEDGE of acid-base behavior in solution is essential to the understanding and application of organic functional group methods of analysis.

Several classes of organic compounds are sufficiently acidic or basic, under certain conditions, to be determined by direct titration with a basic or acidic titrant. A few of the compounds that can be determined directly in this manner are amines, amides, quaternary ammonium hydroxides, carboxylic acids, enols, phenols, and the acidic esters of sulfuric and phosphoric acids

In addition to the acidic and basic substances, many compounds that are too weakly acidic or basic to be titrated directly can be reacted with a reagent to produce a measurable change in the acid-base characteristics of the system. In this indirect approach, the change can involve an acidic or basic reagent, or the formation of an acidic or basic product of the reaction. Examples of the indirect acid-base methods are:

1. Reaction with acidic or basic reagents
   (a) Determination of epoxides

   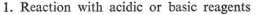

   (b) Saponification of esters

2. Formation of acidic or basic products
   (a) Acetylation of alcohols

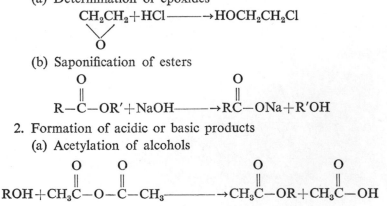

[6]

(b) Hydrolysis of imines

$$\underset{\text{H}}{\text{R}-\text{C}}=\text{N}-\text{R}'+\text{HOH}\longrightarrow \underset{\text{H}}{\text{R}\text{C}}=\text{O}+\text{R}'\text{NH}_2$$

The changes in acid-base characteristics illustrated by these examples can be measured by acidic or basic titrants and, therefore, the reacting compounds themselves can be determined indirectly by an acid-base method.

Because of the large number of organic compounds that can be determined by acid-base methods, a discussion of some of the more important acid-base principles will be given in this chapter. In addition, methods used for the direct titration of acidic and basic substances will be discussed. Many of these direct acid-base procedures are also valuable as end-determinations in the indirect acid-base methods as will be observed in subsequent chapters of this book.

SELECTION OF ACID-BASE METHOD

The selection of the best acid-base method for a particular purpose will depend upon several factors. If the compound to be determined is sufficiently acidic or basic to be titrated directly the following factors must be taken into consideration:

1. The acid-base strength of the compound,
2. The solubility of the compound and its salts in various solvents,
3. The presence of other acidic or basic substances in the sample.

The acid-base strength of the compound to be titrated will predominantly govern the solvent system selected for the titration. If the substance is a weak base, such as aniline, then an acidic solvent, like acetic acid, is desirable in order to enhance the basicity to a point that the titration is feasible. On the other hand, if the substance is an aliphatic amine, like ethylamine, the base strength is such that a wider choice of solvents is available.

Titrations of the aliphatic amines can be performed satisfactorily in neutral solvents, water, slightly basic solvents and acidic solvents. The actual choice of the solvent in this case will be governed by other factors, i.e. solubilities and the presence of interferences.

Similar considerations must be given to the selection of the correct solvent for the titration of acidic compounds.

Most carboxylic acids are sufficiently acidic so that they can be titrated satisfactorily in a wide variety of solvents including water, basic, neutral, and slightly acidic materials. However, basic media, such as pyridine, are usually required for the weaker aromatic hydroxylic acids, like phenol.

Relative Acidities

The prediction of the relative strengths of acids and bases in nonaqueous media from their dissociation constants in water is not always possible, because structural effects may occur to a greater or lesser degree in nonaqueous media than in water. However, such predictions can be very useful as first approximations provided that their limitations are understood.

The relative acidities of a wide variety of organic acids have been studied in pyridine medium and compared with the corresponding acidities in water [12,14]. In general, accurate predictions can be made as to the relative acidities in pyridine, provided that the dissociation constants in water are known and the structures of the acids are taken into consideration.

Acidity studies in pyridine medium have been made by potentiometric titration of the acids with tetrabutylammonium hydroxide. Measurements of the acidity of acids in this medium are compared with the half-neutralization potential, *HNP*, of benzoic acid, which is arbitrarily assigned a value of zero. This technique is used to eliminate day to day variations in liquid-junction potentials.

When the acidities in pyridine, relative to benzoic acid, are compared to the dissociation constants in water, most monofunctional acids fall on one of the three curves in Fig. 1. The three categories of acids that are described by Fig. 1 are:

(1) The *ortho*-substituted benzoic acids (Curve 1),

(2) Monocarboxylic acids and the *meta*-and *para*-substituted benzoic acids (Curve 2),

(3) *Ortho*, *meta*, or *para*-substituted phenols (Curve 3).

Within any of these three categories of acids, the acidities in pyridine relative to that in water remain constant. For example, acetic acid and p-nitrobenzoic acids have pK_a's in water of 4.70 and 3.42 respectively. Reference to Curve 2 in Fig. 1 shows that the *HNP* of acetic acid in pyridine would be approximately 80 mv while the corresponding value for p-nitrobenzoic acid would be 110 mv. Thus, in water as in pyridine, p-nitrobenzoic acid is the stronger acid.

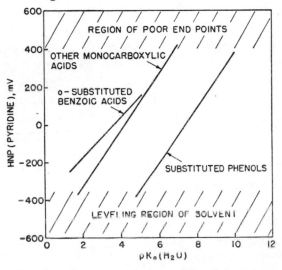

FIG. 1. Relative acidities in pyridine and water

The influence of the structure of acids on their relative acidities is illustrated by comparing the acidities of p-nitrobenzoic and o-chlorobenzoic acids in water and pyridine. The pK_a of p-nitrobenzoic acid is 3.42, as previously mentioned, while the pK_a of o-chlorobenzoic acid is 2.94. Thus, in water, the latter acid is the stronger. The *HNP* of p-nitrobenzoic acid in pyridine is 110 mv, while reference to Curve 1 shows the *HNP* of o-chlorobenzoic acid to be 75 mv. In pyridine medium, therefore, inversion of acidities occur, and p-nitrobenzoic acid is the stronger acid.

Comparative acidity studies such as this are invaluable to the selection of conditions for the titration of acidic substances.

The pyridine information is particularly valuable since pyridine is an excellent medium for the titration of acids.

From a knowledge of the dissociation constant of an acid in water and by reference to Fig. 1, it is possible to determine whether pyridine would be a satisfactory medium for the titration of acids that fall within the structural types listed.

Most o-, m-, and p-substituted benzoic and monocarboxylic acids are sufficiently strong in pyridine medium to be within the useful potential range of the solvent as illustrated by Fig. 1. However, Curve 2 shows that a hypothetical monocarboxylic acid or m-, or p-substituted benzoic acid with a pK_a in water of 7 would be too weakly acidic in pyridine to give sharp end points.

With substituted phenols, acids with pK_a's less than 9.5 will give relatively sharp potentiometric breaks. Phenols with pK_a's greater than 10 are too weakly acidic in this medium, and can be more successfully titrated in a more basic solvent such as ethylenediamine.

The effect of the aqueous dissociation constant on the sharpness of the potentiometric break in pyridine is illustrated by the curves in Fig. 2 for p-methoxyphenol, $pK_a = 10.16$; and m-nitrophenol, $pK_a = 8.35$.

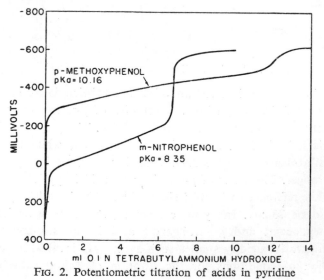

FIG. 2. Potentiometric titration of acids in pyridine

Relative Basicities

The first study of relative basicities in nonaqueous media was performed in glacial acetic acid using perchloric acid as titrant for obtaining the neutralization curves [7]. In this study the absolute potential at the half-neutralization point *HNP* was taken as a measure of the basicity of the amines studied. The curve in Fig. 3 is a plot of *HNP* vs. the pK_a of the amines in water. The basicity of compounds in acetic acid medium is a linear function of the corresponding pK_a's in water for compounds with pK_a (water) less than 4.0 (*p*-bromoaniline = 3,91). With compounds of greater base strength in water than pyridine (pK_a = 5.21), the basicities in acetic acid medium are the same because these bases are ionized to such a large extent in the acidic medium. The leveling of acid-base strengths by the solvent is usually referred to as the leveling effect.

Glacial acetic acid is an excellent solvent for determining total basicities because of the leveling effect. However, the medium is not particularly useful for distinguishing between different basic species because of this effect. The medium can be used satisfactorily for the titration of bases with pK_a (water) greater than approximately 2.3. As indicated in Fig. 3 the potentiometric titration of weaker bases gives poorly defined end points.

Data on relative basicities in several non-protolytic solvents are available. In each of these cases the relative basicities

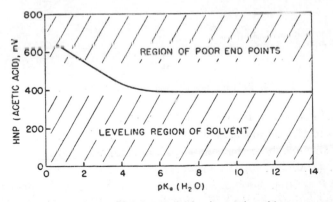

FIG. 3. Relative basicities in acetic acid

of a given structural class are a linear function of the corresponding pK_a's in water.

Data on relative basicities in nitromethane are typical of most non-protolytic solvents [13]. The relative basicities in nitromethane of most monofunctional aliphatic and aromatic amines as compared to their pK_a's in water are described by Curve 1 in Fig. 4. The relative basicities, HNP, in this case are based upon a value of zero for the half-neutralization potential of diphenylguanidine $pK_a(H_2O) = 10.0$

Separate linear relationships between basicities in nitromethane and pK_a's in water are obtained for amides. Curve 2, and heterocyclic amines, hydroxyamines, and diamines, Curve 3.

Within any of the three classes of bases described by the curves in Fig. 4, the basicities in nitromethane relative to that in water

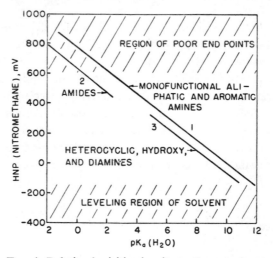

FIG. 4. Relative basicities in nitromethane and water

remain constant. However, inversion of basicities does occur from class to class. For example, in water diphenylamine ($pK_a = 0.85$) is a stronger base than urea ($pK_a = 0.50$) while in nitromethane urea (HNP = 590) is considerably stronger than diphenylamine (HNP = 701). Similar inversions occur between the monofunctional amines and the hydroxyamines or the diamines.

The non-protolytic solvents nitromethane and acetonitrile can be used for the titration of a wide variety of bases. Such solvents are particularly useful for resolving bases of different strengths because leveling does not occur except for bases with pK_a's (H_2O) greater than approximately 12. The solvents can also be used for amines with pK_a's (H_2O) greater than 2, and for amides with pK_a's (H_2O) greater than 0.5.

Some bases that are too weak to be titrated in acetonitrile, nitromethane, or acetic acid can be titrated satisfactorily in the non- protolytic solvent acetic anhydride [11]. This solvent can be used successfully for amines or amides with pK_a's (H_2O) greater than 2.0. Also in this solvent leveling does not occur for amines with pK_2's (H_2O) less than 10; therefore, the solvent can be used for distinguishing between bases. The disadvantage of the solvent is its reactivity. Primary and secondary amines are acetylated by the solvent to produce weaker bases.

DIFFERENTIATIONS

If the difference in strengths of a pair of acidic or basic substances is sufficiently great, the specific determination of one or both of the substances by an acid-base titration is possible. Such determinations are commonly referred to as differentiating titrations or differentiations. In such determinations the ability to differentiate between the pair will be predominantly governed by the solvent employed for the titration. Solvents that are neither acidic or basic are usually best for differentiating titrations, because they do not enhance or reduce the strength of the species to be determined.

Bases

Solvents such as glacial acetic acid level bases to the extent that most amines in this system are essentially of the same strength. Reference to Fig. 3 shows that bases with pK_a's (H_2O) greater than 4.8, i.e. pyridine, are of the same strength in this medium. Figure 3 shows that acetic acid does not level all bases and even in this medium a certain amount of differentiation is possible. In acetic acid medium, bases with pK_a's (H_2O) of less than 0.8

and greater than 4.8 should exhibit sufficiently different strengths so that the direct titration of each base would be possible. However, the determination of the weaker base would not be practical because a poorly defined end point would be obtained. Therefore, acetic acid is not a very good differentiating solvent because the useful range of the solvent is limited by the leveling effect.

Differentiation of bases is much more practical in non-protolytic solvents like acetonitrile [3], and nitromethane [13]. Leveling does not occur, except for the strongest bases, and the solvents can be used to titrate very weak bases i.e., pK_a (H_2O) greater than 2.0.

Since the strengths of most monofunctional amines in non-protolytic solvents are directly related to their pK_a's in water (Fig. 4), predictions as to the practicability of differentiations can be made from a knowledge of the aqueous base strengths of the species to be determined.

The degree of differentiation exhibited by a solvent is related to the slope of curves such as the plots in Figs. 1, 3, and 4. The theoretical slope for a plot of the half-neutralization potential in water vs. pK_a (H_2O) is 59 mv. For solvents of greater resolving power than water the slope is greater than this value.

In water, a degree of differentiation of bases can be obtained with a pK_a difference of approximately 3.0. However, accurate results for the resolution of two bases usually requires a pK_a (H_2O) difference of 4.0. In the following paragraphs, estimates of the differences in strengths required for differentiation are also based upon a sufficient difference to obtain accurate results.

The slope of the curves (Fig. 4) for nitromethane is approximately 78 mv. Therefore, this medium is a slightly better differentiating solvent than water for monofunctional amines. A difference of approximately 260 mv in half-neutralization potential is required for successful differentiation. This corresponds to a pK_a (H_2O) difference of 3.5.

Nitromethane is a poorer medium than water for the differentiation of mixtures of monofunctional amines and heterocylic amines, hydroxyamines, or diamines. The latter three classes of amines (Curve 3) are, relative to monofunctional amines, stronger bases in nitromethane than in water. Therefore, a greater difference in pK_a (H_2O) is required for the resolution of a mixture of a heterocylic amine and a monofunctional aliphatic amine. Assuming that a half-neutralization potential difference of 260 mv is required, this corresponds to a pK_a (H_2O) difference of 4.4. In water a similar degree of resolution would be obtained with a pK_a difference of only 4.0. Similarly nitromethane is also a poorer medium for the resolution of amides and amine pairs. However, such a determination in water is even less practical because amides are too weakly basic and poorly defined end points (or none at all) are obtained.

Acetonitrile is very similar to nitromethane as a differentiating medium. The slope of the HNP (acetonitrile) vs. pK_a (H_2O) curve is 77 mv [6]. Therefore a pK_a (H_2O) difference of 3.5 ($HNP =$ 260 mv) is required for the successful differentiation of monofunctional aliphatic or aromatic amines.

As is the case in nitromethane, a separate relationship exists between HNP (acetonitrile) and pK_a (H_2O) for heterocyclic, hydroxy, and diamines. These bases are, relative to the monofunctional amines, stronger in acetonitrile than in water. Because of this effect, water is a better differentiating medium than acetonitrile for pairs of monofunctional and hydroxyamines. The curves in Fig. 5 illustrate this point. In water, two distinct end points are obtained for the titration of a mixture of triethylamine and triethanolamine (ΔpK_a (H_2O) = 2.82). In acetonitrile, the end point for the titration of triethylamine is obscure.

While the resolution of essentially equimolar concentrations of bases in the non-protolytic solvents is only slightly better than in water and in some cases even worse, such solvents are usually much more practical for differentiations because of two factors: (1) the non-protolytic solvents are better for titrating weak bases and (2) concentration effects are not nearly as pronounced in these solvents.

In the titration of a basic material in the presence of a weaker base, in dilute solutions and at essentially equimolar concentrations, the degree of influence of the weaker base on the titration of the former is not greatly dependent upon solvent effects, provided the media are not appreciably acidic or basic. However, when the weaker base is present at significantly greater concentrations than the stronger base the solvent selected will determine the success of the titration. Larger amounts of extraneous weakly basic substances can be tolerated in nonaqueous media than can be tolerated in water, without affecting the end point of the base being titrated. Also, certain nonaqueous solvents show less of this concentration effect than others. The non-protolytic

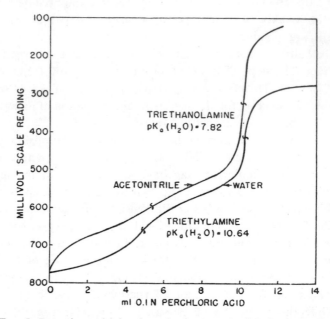

FIG. 5. Potentiometric titration of mixtures of triethylamine and triethanolamine

solvents are particularly good in this respect while solvents like methanol behave like water. An example of this is shown in Fig. 6 for the titration of triethylamine in the presence of a large concentration of diethylacetamide. When the amide concentration is 1000 times that of the amine, the break in acetonitrile is much better than in methanol. At equimolar concentrations, however, very little difference would be noted.

The explanation of the effect of concentration on the ability to differentiate between species of different acid-base strength probably lies in the interaction of the solvent with the acidic and basic species. The effect is less noticable in non-solvating solvents, like acetonitrile; therefore, these solvents are usually preferred for differentiations.

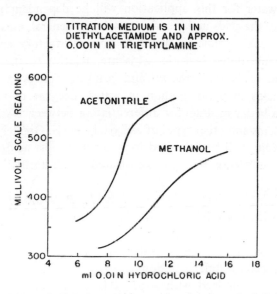

FIG. 6. Effect of diethylacetamide on the titration of triethylamine

Acids

Ethylenediamine should level acids in a manner analogous to the leveling of bases in acetic acid medium, although no data are available for acid strengths in this medium. If analogies are drawn from the acetic acid system, however, acids with pK_a (H_2O) greater than 9 should have similar acidities. With the weaker acids a certain amount of differentiation should be possible. As with acetic acid, ethylenediamine has little practical value as a differentiating medium because of the large leveling effect.

Differentiation of acids is much more practical in pyridine medium. Leveling does not occur except for the strongest acids (see Fig. 1). The monocarboxylic acids with pK_a (H_2O) of greater than 2.0 are not leveled and most acids of this class are within the differentiating range of the solvent.

The substituted phenols are, relative to the monocarboxylic acids, stronger acids in pyridine than in water. Therefore, water may be a better differentiating medium than pyridine for distinguishing between a monocarboxylic acid and phenol. The usefulness of water for this application will be dependent upon the strength of the acids under consideration. In general, most phenols are too weakly acidic in water to give satisfactory end points.

The o-substituted benzoic acids are, relative to the aliphatic carboxylic acids (and the m- and p-substituted benzoic acids) weaker acids in pyridine than in water. Because of this effect water is a better medium for differentiating between o-substituted benzoic acids and other types of carboxylic acids. Greater differences in acidity will be exhibited in water and most acids of these types are sufficiently strong to be titrated satisfactorily in aqueous medium.

In pyridine medium, the slope of the HNP vs. pK_a (H_2O) curve for aliphatic carboxylic acids and the m- and p-substituted benzoic acids is 147 mv. Therefore, within this class of acids differentiation is approximately 2.4 times better in pyridine medium than in water. Successful differentiation in pyridine within this class of acids can be obtained with a pK_a (H_2O) difference of only 2.5. A similar degree of differentiation in water requires a pK_a difference of 4.0

The high resolving power of pyridine is markedly illustrated by the potentiometric titration curves in Fig. 7 for a mixture of dichloroacetic (pK_a (H_2O) = 1.3) and acetic (pK_a (H_2O) = 4.70) acids. In pyridine medium excellent differentiation is obtained while in water the end point for dichloroacetic acid is barely discernable. Differentiation between pairs of o-substituted benzoic acids is not as good as for the other classes of acids, because the slope of the HNP vs. pK_a (H_2O) curve is 112 mv vs. 142 mv for the other acids. However, even for these acids the resolving power in pyridine is 1.8 times that of water.

The slope of the HNP vs. pK_a (H_2O) curve for the substituted phenols is essentially the same as for the aliphatic and m- and p-substituted benzoic acids. Good differentiation between substituted phenols requires a pK_a (H_2O) difference of only 2.5.

Some differentiation is possible with even less differences in pK_a (H_2O) but the analytical results are usually not precise.

Very little work has been done on differentiation of acids in media other than pyridine. Among some of the solvents investigated are acetonitrile, methyl isobutyl ketone, and dioxane. However,

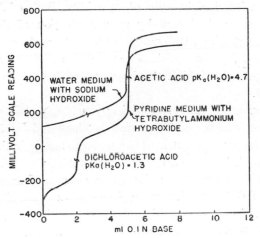

FIG. 7. Potentiometric titration of a mixture of dichloroacetic and acetic acids

none of these solvents has been investigated as fully as pyridine but, based upon the limited data available, they are also effective as differentiating solvents for acids.

It is interesting to note that the differentiation of acids in nonaqueous media is generally much more successful than is the corresponding differentiation of bases. The reason for this effect is not understood.

Interferences

The preceding sections have dealt with the differentiation between species of the same charge-type but with different ionization constants. In the development of many functional group methods of analysis, interference from species of charge-type opposite to that being determined must also be eliminated. The specific determination of tertiary amines by the acetylation of primary and secondary amines, and subsequent acid-base titration is an

2*

example of a method in which both types of interferences are present. The reaction of a primary or secondary amine with acetic anhydride produces a mole of amide and acetic acid. Large concentration of amides can interfere in the determination of the tertiary amines by virtue of their basicity. The acetic acid formed can interfere because of its acidity. Both of these interferences can be eliminated by proper selection of the reaction and titration medium. Differentiating solvents, such as acetonitrile, are preferred for distinguishing between the amines and amides. Such solvents also inhibit the interference due to the acidity of acetic acid.

In water, acetic acid is sufficiently acidic to affect adversely the titration of amines. This effect is illustrated by Curve 1 in Fig. 8 for the potentiometric titration of ethylamine in the presence of acetic acid. In this particular case an excess of ethylamine is present and the first end point corresponds to free ethylamine. The second end point is due to the titration of ethylammonium acetate. In the determination of ethylamine in the presence of a molar excess of acetic acid, only one end point would be obtained, and the sharpness would be dependent upon the acetic acid concentration. For this reason such a determination is not practical.

In the differentiating solvents, acetic acid is not sufficiently acidic to interfere in the titration of amines. This is illustrated by Curve 2 in Fig. 8 for the titration of ethylamine in the presence of acetic acid, in the differentiation solvent methyl Cellosolve. In contrast to the curve obtained in aqueous medium only one break is obtained and this corresponds to the total ethylamine concentration. Even high (up to 20 per cent in the medium) concentrations of acetic acid have little effect upon the titration.

Because weak acids ($pK_a(H_2O)$ greater than 4) are not sufficiently acidic in the differentiating solvents to influence the titration of bases, these solvents are employed frequently in functional group methods of analysis. When interference from stronger acids is encountered, acidic solvents such as glacial acetic acid must be used. In this solvent, acids weaker than nitric will not interfere in the titration of bases.

Interferences from basic substances are frequently encountered in the determination of acids. An example of a functional group method in which such an interference is encountered, is the determination of primary and secondary amines in the presence of tertiary amines by acetylation with acetic anhydride, hydrolysis

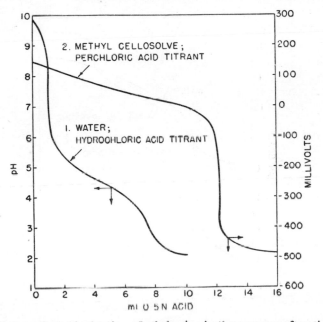

FIG. 8. Potentiometric titration of ethylamine in the presence of acetic acid

of the excess anhydride with water, and titration of the acetic acid formed. The unreacted tertiary amine can affect adversely the titration of acetic acid in aqueous media because of its basicity. This interference is eliminated by using a titration medium consisting essentially of pyridine. Under these conditions the amine is not sufficiently basic to interfere.

The effect of amines on the titration of acids is illustrated by the curves in Fig. 9 for the titration of acetic acid in the presence of ethylamine in water and 75 v/v per cent pyridine. In water only one break is obtained which corresponds to the titration of free acetic acid. The end point for the titration of ethylammonium acetate (total acid) is obscured. In predominantly pyridine medium, two end points are obtained which correspond to the free and total acetic acid content. The latter end point is sufficiently sharp for accurate analysis. If the amount of pyridine in the medium were increased, the second break would become sharper and the first break would eventually disappear.

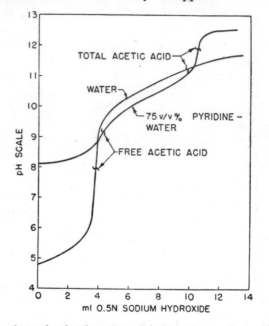

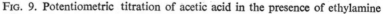

FIG. 9. Potentiometric titration of acetic acid in the presence of ethylamine

Basic nonaqueous solvents are excellent media for eliminating interferences from amines during the titration of acids. In pyridine medium, using tetrabutylammonium hydroxide titrant, large quantities of amines can be tolerated without affecting the titration. Of course, strong bases like sodium hydroxide will interfere quantitatively in the titration.

INDICATORS

Visual observation of the color changes of an indicator is the most simple and usually the most rapid means of detecting the end point of acid-base titrations. If the potentiometric end point is well defined and the indicator transition coincides with the end point, indicators are capable of giving accurate results.

The successful use of an indicator in an acid-base titration will depend upon: (1) The sharpness of the potentiometric end point and (2) the availability of an indicator with a color transition, in the particular solvent, that exactly coincides with the potentiometric equivalence point.

Indicators are usually selected for a particular acid-base titration by trial and error. Potentiometric titration curves are obtained and the color transitions of a series of indicators are noted to determine if any one coincides with the potentiometric end point. In water, if the pH at the equivalence point is known, the selection of the correct indicator is not difficult because the pH transitions of a wide variety of indicators have been studied. Figure 10 shows the useful pH range in water of several indicators and can be used as a guide to the selection of an indicator to

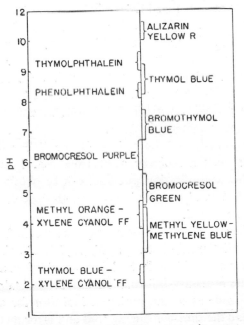

FIG. 10. Indicator transition ranges in water

coincide with the potentiometric end point for acid-base titrations. These particular indicators were selected on the basis of their sharp, easily discernable color changes. The low-pH indicators listed are of little value in water because potentiometric end points in this range are usually not very well defined. However, these indicators are of considerable value in nonaqueous solvents and are listed for this reason.

Very little information is available on indicator scales in non-aqueous media. Indicators are normally selected in these media by the trial and error method using the behavior of the indicators in water as a guide. The indicators listed in Fig. 10 function well in the differentiating solvents and normally retain their relative transition points. If in the evaluation of an indicator for a particular nonaqueous application the transition range of the indicator proves to be too acidic, an indicator above it on the scale should be selected for the next trial.

A more efficient method of selecting indicators in nonaqueous media is illustrated in Fig. 11. In this figure, the useful ranges of indicators in pyridine are listed as a function of the potential of the solutions. As in the study of acidities in pyridine (p. 4), all potential measurements are based upon a value of zero for the half-neutralization potential of benzoic acid. Also, in this figure, the potentials at the neutralization points (NP) for a series of acids are plotted, on a separate curve, as a function of the half-neutralization potential, HNP.

From a knowledge of the pK_a (H_2O) the HNP values can be obtained for most monobasic acids from Fig. 1 as previously discussed. The neutralization potential can be obtained from the relationship in Fig. 11 and the indicator with the correct potential range can be selected.

The selection of indicators for nonaqueous media from a knowledge of the relationship between pK_a (H_2O) and acidities in the media requires a considerable background of information. However, once the necessary information has been obtained, predictions can be made as to the optimum indicator for a particular application and the time-consuming trial and error method can be avoided.

In the leveling media like glacial acetic acid a single indicator can usually be used for most applications since, as previously discussed, the strengths, and thus the neutralization potentials, of most bases are the same. In glacial acetic acid, crystal violet is usually the preferred indicator, although, *a*-zurine 2G is sometimes used because it is less affected by water and other hydroxylic solvents than crystal violet.

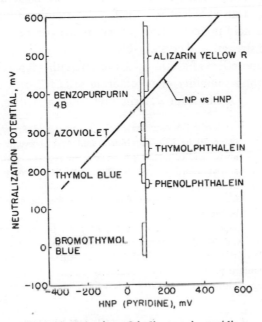

FIG. 11. Behavior of indicators in pyridine

Because ethylenediamine is a leveling solvent for acids, a single indicator is usually satisfactory for titrations in this medium. Either benzopurpurin 4B or orange IV are satisfactory for the titration of acids in ethylenediamine.

METHODS

Some of the more useful acid-base methods are described in this section, although by no means do these represent the only useful techniques for titrating acids and bases. The methods presented include specific procedures for determining total acidity, enols, total basicity, and a procedure for differentiating between acidic species. No specific method is given for differentiation of bases, but several media that can be used for this purpose have been discussed previously in this chapter.

Titration of Bases in Acetic Acid

As previously discussed, acetic acid levels most amines and, therefore, is an excellent solvent for determining total basicities. Perchloric acid in acetic acid is used as the titrant because of its great acid strength and crystal violet is usually used as the indicator. The leveling effect of acetic acid, the strength of perchloric acid, and the good solubility of perchlorate salts in acetic acid makes this an ideal method for determining total basicities.

> *Reagents.*   Standard 0.1 N perchloric acid in acetic acid. Prepare the reagent using 70 to 72% perchloric acid and Grasselli reagent grade acetic acid or equivalent. Allow the regeant to stand overnight and standardize against Bureau of Standards potassium acid phthalate using crystal violet indicator. Heat the solution (do not use an open flame) to dissolve the standard and cool before titrating.
>
> Crystal violet indicator, 1% solution in acetic acid.
>
> *Procedure.*   Add 50 ml. of glacial acetic acid to an Erlenmeyer flask. Add 3 to 4 drops of the crystal violet indicator. Neutralize to the first green color with the standard perchloric acid. Accurately weight 3 to 4 m-equiv. of base into the flask. Titrate with the perchloric acid to the appearance of the first green color.

Scope and Limitations.   Bases with pK_a's (H_2O) greater than approximately 3.0 (ionization constant greater than 1×10^{-11}) can usually be titrated satisfactorily with perchloric acid in acetic acid medium using crystal violet indicator. With weaker bases, poor end points are obtained by the indicator method. When a potentiometric titration is used, the method can be extended to bases with pK_a's (H_2O) greater than 2.0. Standard glass-calomel electrodes are satisfactory for the titration, although better instrument response can be obtained by substituting saturated potassium chloride in methanol for the aqueous electrolyte in the calomel electrode [1].

A few illustrative examples of the many bases that can be titrated in acetic acid medium are listed in Table 1. The total basicity of many polyfunctional amines can be determined in acetic acid medium, provided that the pK_a (H_2O) of each nitrogen is greater than approximately 3.0, and solubility difficulties are circumvented by using a co-solvent. Acetonitrile is essentially neutral to crystal violet, and is effective in inhibiting the precipitation of the perchlorate salts of the amines. When the co-solvent is not present, precipitation may occur before the complete neutralization of all of the amino nitrogens.

TABLE 1

TITRATION OF WEAK BASES IN ACETIC ACID

Compound	Dissociation Constant, H_2O			Number of Groups Titrated
	pKa_1	pKa_2	pKa_3	
Diethylenetriamine	9.85	8.71	3.67	3[a]
N-Phenylpiperazine	8.65	<2.0		1
Aniline	4.58	—		1
Ethylenediamine	9.9	7.05		2[a]
Piperazine	9.65	5.23		2[a]
N-Methylpiperazine	9.02	4.43		2[a]
N-(2-Hydroxyethyl) piperazine	8.98	4.07		2[a]
2,5-Dimethylpyrazine	—	—		1[b]
Calcium acetate	—	—		2
Ammonium chloride	—			1[c]
Sodium chloride	—	—		1[c]
Sodium nitrate	—	—		1

[a] Use 10 ml. of acetonitrile as co-solvent

[b] Titrate in a mixture of 80-20 vol./vol. nitromethane-acetic acid

[c] Add 15 ml. of neutralized 6 per cent mercuric acetate in acetic acid before titration (10)

Certain organic bases can be titrated more effectively in media other than acetic acid. Media that have been used include mixtures of nitromethane with acetic acid and acetic anhydride. Crystal violet indicator can not be used in conjunction with acetic anhydride, and when this solvent is used other indicators must be sough or the potentiometric method employed. Acetic anhydride is effective in eliminating interference from water, while nitromethane actually enhances the basicity of certain types of amines. As discussed previously, heterocyclic amines are stronger bases, relative to the normal amines, in nitromethane than in water or acetic acid. Therefore, some heterocyclic amines can be titrated in nitromethane but not in acetic acid. An example of this is the heterocyclic amine, 2,5-dimethylpyrazine, Table 1. In a mixture of 80–20 v/v per cent nitromethane-acetic acid, good results can be obtained for the titration of one of the nitrogens on this molecule using crystal violet indicator. In acetic acid medium alone, the potentiometric end point is poorly defined. Other heterocyclic bases that have been titrated potentiometrically in nitromethane mixtures are caffeine and 1-methyl-2-pyridone [4].

As illustrated in Table 1, certain salts can be titrated in acetic acid medium. The salts of strong bases and weak acids (nitric or weaker) can be titrated directly. Chloride salts can be titrated by pretreatment of the sample with mercuric acetate [10]. Mercuric acetate reacts with chloride salts to form undissociated mercuric chloride:

(1) $RNH_2 \cdot HCl + Hg(OAc)_2 \longrightarrow RNH_2 + HOAc + HgCl_2$

(2) $NaCl + Hg(OAc)_2 \longrightarrow NaOAc + HgCl_2$

When this technique is used a titratable basic species is formed, while mercuric acetate and mercuric chloride do not interfere in the titration. The technique is particularly useful for analyzing mixtures of amines and their hydrochlorides.

Many nitrogen bases with pK_a's (H_2O) less than 3.0 will interfere in this method because they are too weak to be titrated quantitatively, yet are sufficiently basic to affect the titration of stronger bases. Water and most alcohols are sufficiently basic to interfere in the method, particularly when crystal violet indicator is used. Approximately 1.0 per cent water, and a somewhat higher concentration of alcohols, can be tolerated without interference. The interference of water can be minimized by reacting it with acetic anhydride [5]; however, this technique can not usually be applied to primary or secondary amines.

Acids stronger than nitric are acidic in acetic acid medium and will interfere. Acids included in the "strong " category are hydrochloric, hydrobromic, sulfuric (1H), sulfonic acids, and the acidic esters of sulfuric acid.

Titration of Enols

In basic media compounds possessing the structures

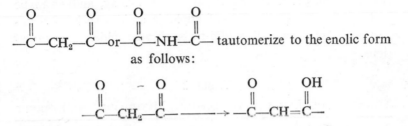

tautomerize to the enolic form as follows:

Although in basic media the enolic form is probably not exclusive, strongly basic titrants will rapidly shift the equilibrium to completion [2].

Media that have been used for the titration of enols are butylamine, ethylenediamine, dimethylformamide, and pyridine. The procedure described here for enols is based upon the titration in pyridine medium with sodium methoxide in pyridine using thymolphthalein indicator.

Reagents. Methanol, anhydrous.
   Pyridine, freshly distilled.
   Standard 0.1 N sodium methoxide in pyridine. Mix 33.4 ml. of 3 N sodium methoxide in methanol (prepared from reagent-grade sodium methoxide) with 40 ml. of methanol and dilute to one liter with pyridine. Standardize daily against benzoic acid using thymolphthalein as the indicator. Add sufficient water during the standardization to inhibit the precipitation of sodium benzoate.
   Thymolphthalein indicator, 1.0% solution in pyridine.

Procedure. Add 25 ml. of pyridine to a 250 ml. glass-stoppered Erlenmeyer flask. Add 2 to 3 drops of the thymolphthalein indicator and neutralize to the first blue color with the standard sodium methoxide. Weigh 3.0 to 4.5 m-equiv. of enolic compound into the flask and titrate to the blue color again. Care should be taken to exclude atmospheric contamination with carbon dioxide during the analysis.

Scope and Limitations. Some enolic compounds that have been titrated successfully by this method are listed in Table 2. Most β-dicarbonyl compounds can be titrated as enols by the

$$
\begin{matrix}
\text{O} & \text{O} \\
\parallel & \parallel
\end{matrix}
$$

method. Compounds of the structure R—C—CH$_2$C—R' are sufficiently acidic if R and R' are alkyl, alkoxy, and aromatic amido nitrogens. Derivatives of aliphatic amides such as acetoacetamide are too weakly acidic to be titrated under these conditions.

TABLE 2

TITRATION OF ENOLS WITH SODIUM METHOXIDE IN PYRIDINE

Compound	Structure of Enol Form
Acetoacetanilide	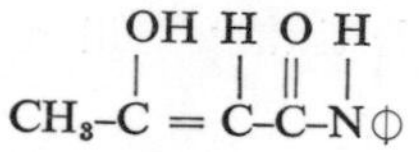 OH H O H | | | | CH$_3$–C = C–C–N Φ
Benzoyl acetone	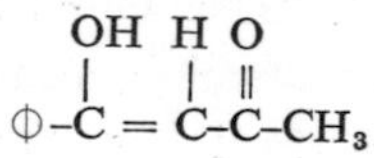 OH H O | | | Φ–C = C–C–CH$_3$
Dehydroacetic acid	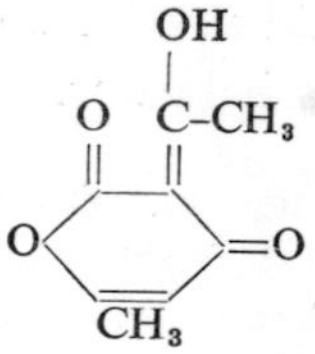 OH | O C–CH$_3$ || || O⟨ ⟩=O CH$_3$
Ethyl acetoacetate	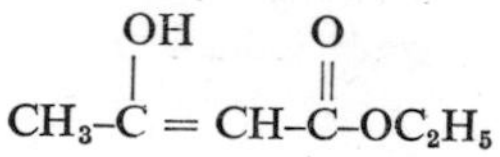 OH O | || CH$_3$–C = CH–C–OC$_2$H$_5$
2,4-Pentanedione	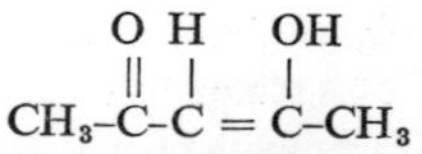 O H OH || | | CH$_3$–C–C = C–CH$_3$

Strong inorganic bases and most acids interfere and can be corrected for. Most aromatic hydroxyl compounds are too weakly acidic to be titrated quantitatively and, therefore, interfere. Organic bases are neutral under the conditions of the titration.

Large quantities of water (more than 5 per cent in the titration medium) interfere by buffering the end point.

Titration of Weak Acids in Ethylenediamine

Ethylenediamine is a strongly leveling solvent; therefore, many acids have similar acidities in this medium. For this reason, ethylenediamine is a good solvent for total acidity determinations. Because of the leveling effect, a single indicator, either benzopurpurin 4B or orange IV, can be used for the titration.

Standard sodium hydroxide in ethylenediamine is used as the titrant in the procedure described here.

Reagents. Ethylenediamine, redistilled, containing less than 2% water.
Methanol, anhydrous.
Benzopurpurin 4B indicator, 0.1% solution in methanol.
Orange IV indicator, 0.1% solution in methanol.
Sodium hydroxide, 0.1 N solution in ethylenediamine. Dissolve 4.0 gm of reagent grade sodium hydroxide in 125 ml. of methanol and dilute to one liter with ethylenediamine. Standardize against benzoic acid dissolved in ethylenediamine and use either benzopurpurin 4B or orange IV indicator.

Procedure. Add 50 ml. of ethylenediamine to a 250-ml. glass-stoppered Erlenmeyer flask. Add 10 drops of the indicator and neutralize with the 0.1 N sodium hydroxide in ethylenediamine. Weigh 2.5 to 4.0 m-equiv. of acid into the flask and titrate again to the end point. Protect the titrant and contents of the titration flask from atmospheric contamination by carbon dioxide.

Scope and Limitations. Most carboxylic acids are sufficiently strong to be titrated in ethylenediamine medium. Although no extensive acidity studies have been made in this medium, most monobasic substituted phenols are sufficiently acidic to be titrated satisfactorily. A few examples of acids that have been titrated are listed in Table 3.

The second hydroxyl of *o-*, *m-*, and *p*-dihydroxy aromatic compounds is too weak to be titrated, but is sufficiently strong to interfere in the titration of the first hydroxyl. Thus, hydroquinone and similar compounds cannot be determined by this method. When the hydroxyl groups are separated by 8 carbon atoms (see Table 3), the neutralization of the first hydroxyl does not influence the second and both are titratable.

Carbon disulfide inteferes by reaction with the solvent to form a dithiocarbamic acid. Organic chlorides react to form hydrogen chloride which interferes. The water concentration in the titration medium should be below 2 per cent, otherwise, the indicator end point is affected. Other hydroxylic compounds also interfere, but to a lesser extent.

TABLE 3

TITRATION OF WEAK ACIDS IN ETHYLENEDIAMINE

Compound	$pKa_1(H_2O)$	$pKa_2(H_2O)$	Number of Groups Titrated
Carbonic acid	6.46	10.36	1
p-Cresol	10.17	—	1
2,4-Dihydroxybenzaldehyde	—	—	1
2,2'-Diphenylolpropane	—	—	2
Di(2-hydroxyphenyl) methane	—	—	1
Di(4-hydroxyphenyl)methane	—	—	2
Hydrogen sulfide	7.04	14.92	1
1-Naphthol	9.85	—	1
Phenol	9.95	—	1
p-Phenylphenol	—	—	1
p-tert-Butylphenol	—	—	1

The ordinary glass-calomel electrodes can not be used for potentiometric titrations with this system because sodium ion presumably poisons the glass electrode. An antimony electrode system, however, has been used satisfactorily [9].

Titration of Acids in Pyridine with Tetrabutylammonium Hydroxide

Pyridine is an excellent medium for the titration of acids, particularly when differentiation between acidic species is desired. Tetrabutylammonium hydroxide has been used as a titrant [1, 8] in conjunction with this medium and has the distinct advantage of forming soluble salts of most acids.

Because the neutralization potentials of many acids differ in pyridine medium, indicators are not specified in the procedure described here, but a method of selecting a satisfactory indicator for the tetrabutylammonium hydroxide-pyridine system is given.

Reagents. Standard 0.1 M tetrabutylammonium hydroxide in benzene. Dilute 100 ml. of 1 M tetrabutylammonium hydroxide in methanol (can be purchased from Southwestern Analytical Chemicals, Austin, Texas) to one liter with benzene and mix. Standardize against benzoic acid in pyridine medium using phenolphthalein indicator.

Pyridine, redistilled.

Indicators, see Fig. 11. Prepare a 0.1% solution of the selected indicator in either pyridine or methanol.

Procedure: Standardization of pH *meter.* Add 0.3 g of benzoic acid, weighed to the nearest 0.1 mg, to a suitable beaker containing 10 ml. of pyridine. Apply a nitrogen purge across the top of the liquid to exclude carbon dioxide. Add a calculated amount of 0.1 M tetrabutylammonium hydroxide to the solution to half-neutralize exactly the benzoic acid. Using a pH meter equipped with glass-modified calomel[1] electrodes, adjust the instrument to read zero on the millivolt scale.

Potentiometric titration. Transfer a weighed sample, containing 0.1 to 0.2 m-equiv. of acidity, to a beaker containing 100 ml. of pyridine. Using a pH meter standardized as described above, titrate the sample with tetrabutylammonium hydroxide and observe the potential reading corresponding to each increment of titrant. Use a nitrogen purge to exclude carbon dioxide. Note the potential at the equivalence point of the titration.

Indicator titration. Using the neutralization potential obtained above, select the proper indicator for the titration by referring to Fig. 11.

Scope and Limitations. A discussion of the effect of pK_a (H_2O) on the ability to titrate acids in pyridine was presented previously in this chapter. The tetrabutylammonium hydroxide-pyridine system is particularly useful for differentiations and the degree to which this is possible was discussed on p. 17.

This procedure should be applicable to the titration of enols and could probably be substituted directly for the sodium methoxide-pyridine method presented in this chapter. However, this possibility has not been investigated.

The strong mineral acids have similar acidities in pyridine medium and therefore can not be differentiated from one another. However, sulfuric acid exhibits two "breaks" in this medium [1] and this allows the determination of sulfuric acid in the presence of other strong monobasic mineral acids.

REFERENCES

1. CUNDIFF R. H., MARKUNAS, P. C., *Anal. Chem.*, **28**, 792 (1956).
2. FRITZ, J. S., *Anal. Chem.* **24**, 674 (1952).
3. FRITZ, J. S., *Anal. Chem.* **25**, 407 (1953).
4. FRITZ, J. S., FULDA, M. O., *Anal. Chem.* **25**, 1837 (1953).
5. GREMILLION, A. F., *Anal. Chem*, **27**, 133 (1955).
6. HALL, H. K., Jr., *J. Phys. Chem.*, **60**, 63 (1956).
7. HALL, N. F., *J. Amer. Chem. Soc.*, **52**, 5115 (1930).
8. HARLOW, G. A., NOBEL, C. M., WYLD, G. E. A, *Anal. Chem* **28**, 787 (1956).
9. MOSS, M. L., ELLIOT, J. H., HALL, R.T., *Anal. Chem.* **20**, 784, (1948)
10. PIFER, C. W., WOLLISH, E. G., *Anal. Chem.* **24**, 300 (1952).
11. STREULI, C. A., *Anal. Chem.*, **30**, 997 (1958).
12. STREULI, C. A., MIRON, R. R., *Anal. Chem.*, **30**, 1978 (1958).
13. STREULI, C. A., *Anal. Chem.*, **31**, 1652 (1959).
14. STREULI, C. A., *Anal. Chem.*, **32**, 407 (1960).

CHAPTER 3

NITROGEN COMPOUNDS

THERE are many different classes of organic compounds containing nitrogen and many of these classes are of considerable commercial importance. Amines comprise the largest and most important class, while other classes of interest include the amides, imines, isocyanates, nitro compounds, and the quaternary ammonium compounds.

Most amines are sufficiently basic so that they can be determined by direct titration with standard acid. The principle of such acid-base titrations and a few methods were presented in Chapter 2. Certain imines are also appreciably basic and can be titrated directly; however, a more satisfactory method is discussed in Chapter 4. The methods for amines presented in this chapter are more specific for the individual types of amines than are the methods based upon the titration of total basicity.

Methods are included in this chapter for the determination of primary, secondary, and tertiary amines, amides, and such miscellaneous compounds as nitriles, nitro compounds, isocyanates, isothiocyanates, and quaternary ammonium compounds. The quaternary ammonium hydroxides, being strong bases, can be titrated directly with standard acids. Also, certain quaternary ammonium salts can be determined either by direct titration or by conversion to the corresponding acetates, with mercuric acetate, and subsequent titration in glacial acetic acid[9]. This procedure was discussed in Chapter 2.

AMINES

Because amines are bases and can be titrated as such, the more difficult analytical problems associated with their analyses usually involve the resolution of mixtures of ammonia, primary (1°),

[35]

secondary (2°), and tertiary (3°) amines. Problems of this type arise because all of these species are often present in varying concentrations in the production of specific amines and are, therefore, often contaminants in the amine products.

Methods are presented in the following sections for the specific determination of primary amines, primary plus secondary amines, secondary amines, secondary plus tertiary amines, and tertiary amines.

2,4-Pentanedione Method for Primary Amines

The enol form of 2,4-pentanedione reacts with 1° amines to form the corresponding imines:

$$CH_3 \overset{\overset{O}{\|}}{-C} -CH = \overset{\overset{OH}{|}}{C} -CH_3 + RNH_2 \rightarrow CH_3 \overset{\overset{N-R}{\|}}{-C} -CH = \overset{\overset{OH}{|}}{C} -CH_3 + H_2O$$

Pentanedione is a weak acid while the imine reaction products are essentially neutral. Therefore, in the method described here[5] an excess of pentanedione is reacted with the primary amine in pyridine medium and the unreacted pentanedione is titrated with standard sodium methoxide using thymolphthalein indicator.

Reagents. 2,4-Pentanedione, commercial grade, Union Carbide Chemicals Company. Distill under atmospheric pressure and at 3 to 1 reflux, using a column having at least 10 theoretical plates. Collect a hearts fraction consisting of approximately one-third of the charge.

2,4-Pentanedione, approximately 2.5 M in pyridine. Prepare from the redistilled pentanedione and redistilled pyridine.

Sodium methoxide, 0.5 N solution in pyridine; Mix 167 ml. of 3 N sodium methoxide (prepared from reagent-grade sodium methoxide) with 40 ml. of methanol and dilute to one liter with pyridine. Standardize daily against benzoic acid using thymolphthalein indicator. Add sufficient water during the standardization to inhibit the precipitation of sodium benzoate.

Thymolphthalein indicator, 1.0% solution in pyridine.

Procedure. Pipet 10.0 ml. of the 2.5 N pentanedione reagent into each of two 250 ml. glass-stoppered Erlenmeyer flasks. For reactions at 90°C, use heat-resistant pressure bottles. Reserve one of the flasks as a blank. Weigh 10 to 15 m-equiv. of primary amine into the other flask. Allow the flasks to stand at the optimum temperature and for sufficient time to obtain quantitative reaction. Consult Table 4 for the reaction conditions for several primary amines. Add 1 ml. of the thymolphthalein indicator to each flask and titrate with the standard sodium methoxide to the appearance of the first definite blue color.

Scope and Limitations. Most primary aliphatic amines react quantitatively with pentanedione under the conditions of the method. Several of the compounds that have been determined by the method are listed in Table 4. The method can be applied to primary amino acids provided that they are first converted to the sodium salts. The free acids react too slowly with the reagent to be determined directly. The method can also be applied to the determination of the alcohol-amines, ethyleneamines, and primary amino compounds that also contain a heterocyclic amino nitrogen. These classes of compounds are difficult to determine by other methods.

The method is not applicable to 1° aromatic amines, and aniline does not react appreciably with the reagent. Also, sterically hindered 1° amines, such as tertiary butylamine, do not react quantitatively with the reagent.

Most acids and strong bases will interfere in the method; however, corrections can usually be applied.

Because the method is based upon a nonaqueous titration, large quantities of water affect adversely the indicator end point. Usually 10 per cent water can be tolerated in the titration medium without serious interference. Considerably larger quantities of other solvents such as alcohols, ketones, 3° amines, esters, and nitriles can be tolerated without interference.

Secondary alcoholamines, such as diethanolamine and diiso-propanol-amine tend to react under the conditions of the method. This interference can be minimized by adjusting the sample size so that at least 10 m-equiv. of 1° amine are present for reaction. In this way, the effective concentration of pentanedione is reduced by reaction with the 1° amine, and interference from the 2° amine is negligible. Because of this interference, the determination of 1° alcohol-amines in the presence of 2° alcoholamines is limited to samples containing more than 5 per cent of the former.

Heterocyclic 2° amines, such as piperazine and morpholine, react slowly with pentanedione. Usually this interference can be inhibited by conducting the reaction at 0°C or by using the technique described for the alcoholamines.

Ammonia reacts quantitatively with the reagent; however, a correction can be applied by determining the ammonia independently by the sodium cobaltinitrate method[7].

TABLE 4

REACTION CONDITIONS FOR DETERMINING PRIMARY AMINES BY REACTION WITH PENTANEDIONE

Compound	Reaction Conditions	
	Temp., °C	Time, min.
Alanine	98	15 to 90[a]
β-Alanine	98	15 to 90[a]
N-Aminoethylpiperazine	0	30 to 60
Ammonia	25	30 to 120
Benzylamine	25	15 to 120
Butylamine	25	15 to 60
Diethylenetriamine	25	15 to 60
Ethanolamine	25	15 to 60[b]
Ethylamine	25	15 to 60
Ethylenediamine	25	30 to 90
2-Ethylhexylamine	25	15 to 60
Glycine	98	60 to 120[a]
Isopropanolamine	25	15 to 60[c]
Methylamine	25	15 to 60
Propylenediamine	25	60 to 120
Tetraethylenepentamine	25	90 to 120

(a) Dissolve the sample in 10 ml. of water, add a calculated equivalent amount of standard 0.5 N sodium methoxide to neutralize the sample, and add 75 ml. of pyridine before titration.

(b) In the presence of over 50% diethanolamine, the sample should contain 10 to 15 m-equiv. of primary amine and the reaction time should be limited to 20 to 30 minutes.

(c) In the presence of over 50% diisopropanolamine, the sample should contain 10 to 15 m-equiv. of primary amine and the reaction time should be limited to 40 to 60 minutes.

Carbon Disulfide Method for Primary and Secondary Amines

Carbon disulfide reacts with 1° and 2° amines to form the corresponding dithiocarbamic acids:

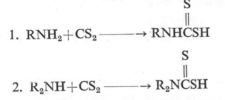

$$1. \ RNH_2 + CS_2 \longrightarrow \overset{\overset{\displaystyle S}{\|}}{RNHCSH}$$

$$2. \ R_2NH + CS_2 \longrightarrow \overset{\overset{\displaystyle S}{\|}}{R_2NCSH}$$

This principle is the basis of the method presented below for determining 1° plus 2° amines [3]. In the method, the amines are converted to the dithiocarbamic acids and the acids are titrated with standard sodium hydroxide using phenolphthalein indicator.

Reagents. Carbon disulfide, reagent grade.
2-Propanol 99%.
Pyridine, redistilled. This material should contain less than 0.001 m-equiv. of 1° and 2° amine per gram as determined by the procedure below.
Standard 0.5 N sodium hydroxide.
Phenolphthalein indicator, 1.0% solution in pyridine.

Procedure. Add the solvent specified in Table 5 to each of two 250-ml. glass-stoppered Erlenmeyer flasks. Reserve one of the flasks as a blank. Weigh no more than 15 m-equiv. of 1° and 2° amine into the other flask. The sample aliquot should contain no more than 30 m-equiv. of ammonia and/or strong (i.e., $pK_a > 7$) 3° amine. If more than 2 m-equiv. of ammonia are present in the sample, cool the contents of the flasks to 10°C. Do not use a dry ice bath. Add 5 ml. of carbon disulfide and swirl the flasks. Add 1 ml. of phenolphthalein indicator and titrate with standard 0.5 N sodium hydroxide to an end point that is stable for at least one minute. For samples that contain more than 2 m-equiv. of ammonia, the titration should be conducted at 0°C. Note: The end point in the titration may be fleeting. The titrant should be added incrementally until a permanent end point is obtained. Stopper the flasks while checking the permanency of the end point so that carbon dioxide is excluded.

Scope and Limitations. The reaction of 1° and 2° amines with carbon disulfide is an equilibrium reaction, and quantitative results can be obtained only by forcing the reaction to completion with the sodium hydroxide titrant. Secondary amines react more completely than 1° amines and the end points for these compounds are readily obtained. With 1° amines, the titrant must be added incrementally in the vicinity of the end point until a stable end point is obtained. Over-addition of the titrant will lead to erroneous results via xanthate formation with the 2-propanol solvent.

Three different solvent combinations are recommended for the various amines listed in Table 5. The pyridine-water-2-p ropa-

TABLE 5

REACTION CONDITIONS FOR DETERMINING PRIMARY AND SECONDARY AMINES BY REACTION WITH CARBON DISULFIDE

Compound	Solvent		
	Pyridine	Water	2-propanol
2-Aminoethylethanolamine	50 ml.	25 ml.	50 ml.
Butylamine	—	—	75 ml.[a]
sec.-Butylamine	25 ml.	—	75 ml.
Dibutylamine	—	—	75 ml.[a]
Diethanolamine	25 ml.	—	75 ml.
Diethylamine	—	—	75 ml[a]
Diethylenetriamine	50 ml.	25 ml.	50 ml.
Di(2-ethylhexyl)amine	25 ml.	—	75 ml.
Dimethylamine	—	—	75 ml.[a]
2,6-Dimethylpiperazine	50 ml.	25 ml.	50 ml.
Ethanolamine	25 ml.	—	75 ml.
Ethylamine	—	—	75 ml.[a]
Ethylenediamine	50 ml.	25 ml.	50 ml.
2-Ethylhexylamine	25 ml.	—	75 ml.
Methylamine	—	—	75 ml.[a]
Morpholine	50 ml.	25 ml.	50 ml.
Propylenediamine	50 ml.	25 ml.	50 ml.

[a] If more than 2 m-equiv. of ammonia and/or strong ($pK_a > 7$) tertiary amines are present, add sufficient pyridine to suppress their basicity.

nol solvent is specified for amines that form insoluble dithiocarbamic acids. 2-propanol is used for the more reactive amines. The pyridine-2-propanol solvent is used for the less reactive amines that form soluble dithiocarbamic acids. When one of these three solvent combinations is used, most aliphatic 1° and 2° amines can be determined by the method. Only the aromatic and sterically hindered aliphatic amines fail to react quantitatively.

Although the reaction of carbon disulfide is fairly specific, there is a tendency for ammonia to react with the reagent. The extent of this interfering reaction is dependent upon temperature and the nature of the solvent. The interference can be inhibited by conducting the reaction and subsequent titration at reduced temperature, and by using a solvent containing a minimum amount of pyridine. Under ideal conditions (simple aliphatic amines) up to 30 m-equiv. of ammonia can be tolerated. If large quantities of pyridine are required for solubilization of the dithiocarbamic acids or for quantitative reaction, less ammonia must be present.

Because the method is based upon an acid-base titration, compounds that are not neutral to the indicator will interfere; however, corrections can usually be applied. The method can be applied to the analysis of mixtures of amines and strong inorganic bases and mixtures of amines and acids. In these applications, the sample is neutralized to the indicator using an appropriate standard acid or base, and then the amines are converted to the dithiocarbamic acids and titrated.

2-Ethylhexaldehyde-Carbon Disulfide Method for Secondary Amines

Primary amines react quantitatively with an excess of 2-ethylhexaldehyde to form the corresponding imines according to the following equation [3]:

$$RNH_2 + C_4H_9\underset{\overset{|}{C_2H_5}}{C}HCH = O \longrightarrow C_4H_9\underset{\overset{|}{C_2H_5}}{C}HCH = NR + H_2O$$

Most secondary amines do not undergo this reaction and can be converted to the dithiocarbamic acids with carbon disulfide. The imines from primary amines do not react with carbon disulfide to form acids and, therefore, do not interfere. The dithiocarbamic acids of the secondary amines are titrated with standard sodium hydroxide using phenolphthalein as indicator. Under the conditions of the method, ammonia, most primary amines, and tertiary amines do not interfere, thus providing a specific method for secondary amines.

Reagents. The reagents in this method are the same as in the previous carbon disulfide method with the exception of the following: 2-Ethylhexaldehyde, 50 v/v % pyridine solution containing 0.5% phenyl-1-naphthylamine inhibitor. The acidity in the 2-ethylhexaldehyde should be sufficiently low so that the reagent blank in the following procedure is less than 0.5 ml. Acid-free aldehyde can be prepared by washing with sodium carbonate solution.

Procedure. Pipet 10.0 ml. of the 2-ethylhexaldehyde reagent into each of two 250-ml. glass-stoppered Erlenmeyer flasks. If dimethylamine is being determined, add 50 ml. of 2-propanol. Reserve one of the flasks as a blank. Weigh no more than 13 m-equiv. of secondary amine into the other flask. The combined ammonia and strong ($pK_a > 7$) tertiary amine content should not exceed 30 m-equiv. while the primary amine content should be less than 16 m-equiv. Allow the flasks to stand at room temperature for 5 min. Cool the contents to $-10°C$. Do not use a dry ice bath. Add 5 ml. of carbon disulfide to each flask. Add 1 ml. of phenolphthalein indicator and titrate with standard 0.5 N sodium hydroxide at below $0°C$. The end point should be stable for at least one minute.

Scope and Limitations. Because carbon disulfide reacts quantitatively with most secondary amines (with the exception of aromatic and sterically hindered amines), the limiting factor in this method is the ability to destroy the primary amine, if present, with 2-ethylhexaldehyde without reaction with the secondary amine. Most simple aliphatic primary amines react quantitatively with 2-ethylhexaldehyde under the conditions of the method. The following types of primary amines do not react quantitatively and, therefore, secondary amines cannot be determined if they are present; alcoholamines, aromatic amines, sterically hindered aliphatic amines, and the ethyleneamines. While several other types of secondary amines can be determined, other than those listed in Table 6, only the secondary amines are listed whose corresponding primary amines (or for which no corresponding primary amine exists) react quantitatively with 2-ethylhexaldehyde.

The titration in this method is essentially the same as in the previously presented method for primary and secondary amines; therefore, the interferences are similar.

TABLE 6

REACTION CONDITIONS FOR DETERMINING SECONDARY AMINES
BY THE 2-ETHYLHEXALDEHYDE-CARBON DISULFIDE METHOD

Compound	Titration Solvent		
	Pyridine	Water	Isopropyl alcohol
Dibutylamine	—	—	75 ml.[a]
Diethylamine	—	—	75 ml.[a]
Di(2-ethylhexyl)amine	25 ml.	—	75 ml.
Dihexylamine	—	—	75 ml.[a]
Dimethylamine	—	—	75 ml.[b]
2,6-Dimethylpiperazine	50 ml.	25 ml.	50 ml.
Morpholine	50 ml.	25 ml.	50 ml.

[a] If more than 2 m-equiv. of ammonia and/or strong ($pK_a > 7$) tertiary
amines are present, add sufficient pyridine to suppress their basicity.
[b] Conduct the reaction with 2-ethylhexaldehyde in the presence of 50 ml.
of isopropyl alcohol then add 25 ml. more prior to titration.

Salicylaldehyde Method for Secondary and Tertiary Amines

Salicylaldehyde reacts with primary amines to form the corresponding imines according to the following equation:

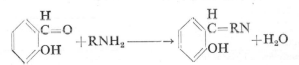

The imines formed in the above reaction are weaker bases than
the parent amines.

This principle was used by Wagner, Brown, and Peters[19] for
determining secondary and tertiary amines in the presence of
primary amines. In their method, the amine mixture is reacted
with salicylaldehyde in methanol medium and the unreacted
secondary and tertiary amines are titrated, potentiometrically,
with standard hydrochloric acid in 2-propanol.

The Wagner, Brown, and Peters method is not applicable to
aromatic amines; therefore, Siggia, Hanna, and Kervenski[12]
modified the method to include these compounds. In their modification, a mixture of ethylene glycol and 2-propanol is used

as the solvent for the reaction and the titrant. The procedure of Siggia, Hanna, and Kervenski is described below:

Reagents. Ethylene glycol-2-propanol solvent, 50–50 v/v % solution. Standard 1 N hydrochloric acid in the ethylene glycol-2-propanol solvent. Standardize against tris (hydroxymethyl)-amino-methane (Fisher's Certified Reagent) in water using bromo-cresol green indicator.

Salicylaldehyde (from bisulfite addition compound).

Procedure. Transfer 50 ml. of the ethylene glycol-2-propanol solvent to a 250-ml. tall form beaker. Weigh 20 m-equiv. of secondary and/or tertiary amine into the beaker. The sample should contain no more than 35 m-equiv. of primary amine. Add 5 ml. of salicylaldehyde. Stir the solution and allow it to stand for 30 minutes at room temperature. Titrate with the standard 1 N hydrochloric acid potentiometrically using a pH meter equipped with glass-calomel electrodes.

Scope and Limitations. The salicylaldehyde method of Siggia, Hanna, and Kervenski is applicable to a wide variety of secondary amines, a few of which are listed in Table 7. The major disadvan-

TABLE 7

SECONDARY AND TERTIARY AMINES THAT CAN BE DETERMINED BY THE SALICYLALDEHYDE METHOD

Aliphatic and Alicyclic Amines	Aromatic Amines
Diethylenetriamine	Diethylaniline
N, N-Dimethylcyclohexylamine	Diethyl-1-naphthylamine
N, N-Dimethyllaurylamine	Dimethylaniline
N-Ethylpiperidine	Dimethyl-1-naphthylamine
Dibutylamine	Ethylaniline
N-Methylcyclohexyalamine	Ethyl-1-naphthylamine
N-Methyllaurylamine	
Piperidine	
Piperizine	
Tributylamine	

tage of the method is that the potentiometric end point leaves something to be desired in the presence of the imine reaction products of some primary amines. The salicylaldehyde-imines of the aliphatic amines are sufficiently strong bases to affect the end point adversely, during the titration of the unreacted secondary or tertiary amines. In fact, many of these amines can be titrated under the conditions of the method and a second "break" is evident after the end point for the secondary or tertiary amine. This second "break" can be used as a measure of the primary amine content of the sample; however, the end points are usually not sufficiently well defined for accurate results.

Although indicators cannot normally be applied to this method, the procedure is of considerable value, since it can be applied in many cases where other secondary amines methods, such as the 2-ethylhexaldehyde-carbon disulfide method, fail.

Ammonia does not react quantitatively with salicylaldehyde and will interfere in the method unless removed before the analysis. The method, also, cannot be applied to the analysis of mixtures of the alcoholamines because of a side reaction with the secondary alcoholamine. Because the method is based upon an acid-base titration, materials that are not neutral under the conditions of the titration interfere. Interferences of this type are the mineral acids and the strong inorganic bases; however, corrections can be applied for these compounds.

Titration of Tertiary Amines After Acetylation of Primary and Secondary Amines

Most methods for the specific determination of tertiary amines are based upon the acetylation of the sample, and the subsequent titration of the unreacted tertiary amines. Under the conditions of the methods, ammonia and primary and secondary amines are converted to amides which are considerably weaker bases than the tertiary amines. Methods of this type depend upon the ability to differentiate between the tertiary amine and the amides formed; therefore, the differentiating powers of the solven system used governs the success of the methods. For this reason, acidic solvents like acetic acid are not of general applicability because they enhance the basicity of the amides to such an extent that poorly defined end points are obtained for the titration of the tertiary amine. The neutral solvents such as alcohols and aceto-nitrile are commonly used for determinations of this type.

In the method described here[10], the acetylation and subsequent titration are conducted in methyl Cellosolve; standard perchloric acid in methyl Cellosolve is used as the titrant. Either thymol blue or congo red indicator is used depending upon the strength of the tertiary amine being titrated. Two titrant strengths are specified in the procedure so that both macro and low (0.005 to 1.0 per cent) concentrations of tertiary amines can be determined.

Reagents. Acetic anhydride, 99%.

Methyl Cellosolve. 100 ml. of this solvent should give a blank of less than 0.5 ml. of 0.01 N perchloric acid by the procedure below.

Standard 0.5 N perchloric acid in methyl Cellosolve. Prepare from 70 to 72% perchloric acid and standardize against tris (hydroxymethyl)aminomethane (Fisher's Certified Reagent) in water using bromocresol green indicator.

Standard 0.01 N perchloric acid in methyl Cellosolve. Prepare by dilution of the stronger reagent. Standardize against tris (hydroxymethyl)aminomethane.

Congo red indicator, 0.1% solution in methanol.

Thymol blue indicator, 0.3% solution in dimethylformamide.

Procedure. Add 100 ml. of methyl Cellosolve to each of two 250-ml. glass-stoppered Erlenmeyer flasks. Reserve one of the flasks as a blank. If the 0.5 N titrant is to be used, weigh no more than 15 m-equiv. of tertiary amine into the other flask. No more than 0.3 m-equiv. of tertiary amine should be used with the 0.01 N titrant. The sample should consume no more than 50% of the acetic anhydride. Carefully add 20 ml. of acetic anhydride to each flask. Allow the flasks to stand for 30 min at room temperature (do not cool). Add six drops of the appropriate indicator to each flask. Use thymol blue for amines with $pK_a(H_2O) > 6.5$ and congo red for amines with $pK_a(H_2O) < 6.5$. Titrate the contents of each flask with the appropriate strength standard perchloric acid in methyl Cellosolve.

Scope and Limitations. With the proper selection of titrant strength, this method can be used to determine the purity of tertiary amines and concentrations as low as 0.005 per cent in the presence of primary and secondary amines. The method can be used for the latter application, because large quantities of amide have little effect upon the titration of the tertiary amine in methyl Cellosolve medium. Such is not the case in other media that have been proposed for tertiary amine determinations.

Because of the wide differences in base strengths that are encountered, no single indicator will coincide with the potentiometric end point for the titration of all tertiary amines. For this reason, two separate indicators are specified: (1) thymol blue to cover the range $pK_a(H_2O)$ 11.0 to 6.5, and (2) congo red $pK_a(H_2O)$ 6.5 to 4.0 (See Table 8). Tertiary amines with pK_a (H_2O) less than 4.0 are too weakly basic to be titrated in the solvent system used.

TABLE 8

INDICATORS FOR DETERMINING TERTIARY AMINES AFTER
ACETYLATION OF PRIMARY AND SECONDARY AMINES IN METHYL
"CELLOSOLVE"

Compound	pKa(H₂O)	Indicator
N, N-Dimethylaniline	~4	Congo red
N, N-Dimethylethanolamine	9.21	Thymol blue
N-Ethylmorpholine	7.49	Thymol blue
γ-Picoline	6.04	Congo red
Pyridine	5.23	Congo red
Triethanolamine	7.65	Thymol blue
Triethylamine	10.76	Thymol blue

The method is not applicable to the determination of tertiary amines in the presence of the ethyleneamines because these compounds do not acetylate quantitatively. Such determinations can be performed, however, by using phenylisothiocyanate as the acylating reagent and methanol as the medium.

The alkali metal and alkaline earth hydroxides and organic acid salts will interfere quantitatively in the method, as will the strong mineral acids. Interferences can also be encountered from primary and secondary amines that do not acetylate quantitatively such as the ethyleneamines.

Colorimetric Determination of Primary Amines

Low concentrations (0.01 to 0.5%) of primary amine in the presence of other amines cannot be determined conveniently by any of the volumetric methods previously discussed. Determinations in this concentration range are usually better by colorimetric methods.

One specific colorimetric method that has been proposed for determining primary amines is based upon the formation of the copper complex of the salicylaldehyde-imines[4]:

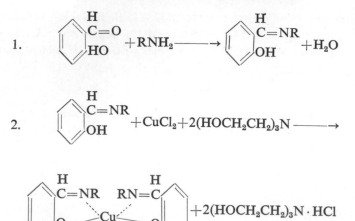

1.

2.

The copper complex which is formed in aqueous media is extracted into n-hexanol. An aliquot of the hexanol layer is removed and the copper present as the complex is determined colorimetrically by reaction with N, N-di(hydroxyethyl)dithiocarbamic acid[15]:

Reagents. n-Hexanol.

Triethanolamine. Redistill 98% triethanolamine, under 1 to 2 mm pressure using a column 6 in. long and 30 mm in diameter packed with glass beads and heated by means of resistance wire. Use a 3l. round-bottomed distillation flask fitted with a thermometer well. Stir the contents of the flask by means of a magnetic stirrer. Do not allow the kettle temperature to exceed 185°C during the distillation. An absorbance of 0.65± 0.02 for 0.372 mg of ethanolamine should be obtained (using a Beckman Model B spectrophotometer operating within specifications) when this material is used in the following reagent.

Copper-salicylaldehyde reagent. Add 15 ml. of the redistilled triethanolamine, 0.5 ml. of salicylaldehyde, and 0.25g of cupric chloride ($CuCl_2 \cdot 2H_2O$), in this order, to a 100-ml. glass-stoppered graduated cylinder. Dilute to volume with distilled water.

N, N-Di(hydroxyethyl)dithiocarbamic acid reagent. Prepare a 2 v/v % solution of carbon disulfide in methanol. Prepare a 5 v/v % solution of diethanolamine. Prepare fresh reagent daily by mixing equal volumes of the two solutions.

Procedure. Pipet 2.0 ml. of the copper-salicylaldehyde reagent into each of two 25-ml. glass-stoppered graduated cylinders. Reserve one of the cylinders as a blank. Weigh an amount of sample into the other cylinder that contains no more than the maximum amount of sample specified in Table 9. The sample must not contain more than 0.01 mg of ammonia or 0.5 g of secondary and/or tertiary amine. Dilute to 10 ml. with water and mix. React for the time and at the temperature specified in Table 9. Dilute to 25 ml. with n-hexanol. Stopper the cylinders and shake vigorously 15 to 20 times and allow the layers to separate. Pipet 5 ml. of the N, N-di(hydroxyethyl)dithiocarbamic acid reagent into each of two additional 25-ml. glass-stoppered graduated cylinders. (Note: These cylinders should be rinsed with the dithiocarbamic acid reagent to inhibit contamination from cupric ion.) Pipet 5 ml. of the hexanol layer from the reaction cylinders into the cylinders containing the dithiocarbamic acid reagent. Dilute to 25 ml. with methanol and mix. Determine the absorbance of the sample vs. the blank at 430 mμ using 1 cm spectrophotometric cells. Determine the concentration of primary amine from a calibration curve prepared using the specific amine being determined.

Scope and Limitations. The copper-salicylaldehyde method is applicable to a wide variety of primary amines, a few of which are shown in Table 9. Compounds that react incompletely include the

TABLE 9

REACTION CONDITIONS FOR DETERMINING PRIMARY AMINES BY THE COPPER-SALICYLALDEHYDE METHOD

Compound	Primary Amine mg maximum	Time, min.
2-Aminoethylethanolamine	1.10	30–60
N-Aminoethylmorpholine	0.85	15–60
Butylamine	0.70	15–60
Ethanolamine	0.50[a]	15–60
Ethylamine	0.53	15–60
2-Ethylhexylamine	1.40	15–60
Isoamylamine	1.10	15–45
Isobutylamine	0.90	15–60
Isopropanolamine	0.60	15–60
Methylamine	0.30	15–60
Propylenediamine	0.42[b]	10–20

[a] For the determination of ethanolamine in refined triethanolamine, add 1 g of sodium oxalate to the copper-salicylaldehyde reagent and conduct the reaction at 98°C in unstoppered 50-ml. graduated cylinders.

[b] Conduct the reaction at 98°C in unstoppered 50-ml. graduated cylinders.

aromatic amines, sterically hindered aliphatic amines, and compounds that contain more than one primary amino nitrogen. Propylenediamine is an exception to the latter generalization. Sterically hindered aliphatic amines that do not react quantitatively are tertiary and secondary butylamine and isopropylamine.

The majority of the primary amines react in a similar manner and can be determined using a single calibration curve. Ethanol amine, isopropanolamine, and methylamine are exceptions to this and require the preparation of a separate calibration curve for each compound. The quality of the triethanolamine used in the method will affect the slope of the calibration curve, and for this reason a procedure is given for refining the material. Commercial grade 98 per cent triethanolamine can be used directly in the method; however, a new calibration curve must be prepared for each lot of material.

The difference in the various lots of triethanolamine is probably due to the presence of materials that complex with copper and, therefore, decrease the effective copper concentration. This type of interference can also be encountered when analyzing samples. Sodium oxalate, incorporated into the reagent, is effective in eliminating this type of interference in the analysis of triethanolamine.

Ammonia interferes in the method if more than 0.01 mg is present in the sample aliquot. Secondary and tertiary amines do not interfere if the combined total amount in the sample aliquot does not exceed 0.5 g.

Strong oxidizing or reducing agents can interfere by depleting the copper in the reagent. Materials that form hexanol-soluble complexes with copper will usually give high results, while low results may be obtained if water-soluble complexes are formed.

Resolution of Amine Mixtures

Frequently the need arises to analyze mixtures of ammonia, primary, secondary, and tertiary amines. This occurs because all of these species may be present in production samples of most specific amines. By proper combination of the foregoing procedures, most problems of this type can be solved.

Mixtures of the simple aliphatic amines can be easily analyzed by combinations of the following procedures: (1) The carbon disulfide method for primary plus secondary amines; (2) The 2-ethylhexaldehyde-carbon disulfide method for secondary amines; (3) The specific titration of tertiary amines after acetylation of the sample; and (4) The determination of ammonia as the difference between the sum of (1) and (3) and a total basicity determination.

The alcoholamine mixtures present more of a problem in that the carbon disulfide procedures are not applicable. One scheme that can be used is as follows: (1) The sodium cobaltinitrite method for ammonia (7); (2) The 2,4-pentanedione method for ammonia plus primary amines; (3) The specific determination of the tertiary amines by the acetylation technique; and (4) The determination of the secondary amine by the difference between the sum of (2) and (3) and a total basicity determination. This scheme is adequate except for samples that contain less than 5.0 per cent primary alcoholamine, in which case the pentanedione method cannot be used. The colorimetric copper-salicylaldehyde method can usually be used for determining the primary amine in such samples because the ammonia contents are usually quite low.

Certain of the less sterically hindered aliphatic amines (i.e., isopropylamine) mixtures can be analyzed using the scheme employing pentanedione. However, if this procedure cannot be applied, the salicylaldehyde method for secondary plus tertiary amines can be used. The application of the salicylaldehyde procedure requires that the sample be free of ammonia, or that the ammonia be physically or chemically separated prior to analysis [13]. The following procedures are required for resolution of the components: (1) The salicylaldehyde method; (2) Determine tertiary amine as before; (3) Determine the primary amine as the difference between (1) and a total basicity determination.

Mixtures of aromatic amines can be resolved using the scheme employing salicylaldehyde described above. If the pK_a of the tertiary amine is less than 4, the previously described tertiary amine method will not apply. If such is the case a potentiometric titration can be used in conjunction with the latter method or a more acidic solvent should be used for the titration. Of course if acidic solvents are used, buffered end points may be obtained in the presence of large quantities of the amides from the primary and secondary amines.

AMIDES

Because of the relative stability of amides, very few chemical methods exist for their determination. The most common reactions that compounds of this type undergo is the acidic and basic hydrolysis to the corresponding acid and amine. Primary and secondary amides can be further acylated; however, reactions of this type are not of analytical importance as yet. In the following sections, two relatively general methods are described: (1) A macro method based upon saponification; and (2) A colorimetric method based upon hydroxamic acid formation.

Saponification of Amides

Very few amides can be determined by the conventional saponification procedures because the conditions are not sufficiently drastic. In the procedure described here quantitative saponification is effected by using elevated temperatures. The amide is refluxed in the presence of a measured excess of 1 N potassium hydroxide in diethylene glycol. After the reaction, the excess potassium hydroxide is titrated with standard hydrochloric acid in methanol using alizarin yellow R-xylene cyanol mixed indicator. The following is a modification of the original procedure of Olsen[8].

Reagents. Potassium hydroxide, 1 N solution in diethylene glycol. Dissolve the potassium hydroxide in 40 ml. of water and dilute to 1 l. Hydrochloric acid, 1 N solution in methanol.
Alizarin yellow R-xylene cyanol mixed indicator. Prepare an aqueous solution containing 0.1 wt./vol. % alizarin yellow R and 0.08 wt./vol. % xylene cyanol FF.

Procedure. Pipet 50.0 ml. of the 1 N potassium hydroxide into each of two 300-ml. 24/40 ℥ glass-stoppered Corning alkali-resistant Erlenmeyer flasks. Reserve one of the flasks as a blank. Weigh 35 m-equiv. of the amide into the other flask. Add a few glass beads to each flask and connect the flasks to individual water-cooled West condensers. Reflux the contents of the flasks for sufficient time to obtain quantitative saponification (consult Table 10). Cool the flasks and wash down the inside walls of the condensers with 100 ml. of pyridine. Titrate with the standard 1 N hydrochloric acid in methanol using the alizarin yellow R-xylene cyanol mixed indicator.

Scope and Limitations. Although only a few amides have been determined by this saponification method (see Table 10), however, the method should be applicable to most of these compounds.

TABLE 10

DETERMINATION OF AMIDES BY SAPONIFICATION
WITH POTASSIUM HYDROXIDE
IN DIETHYLENE GLYCOL

Compound	Reflux Time, min.
Acetamide	30
Acetanilide	90
N-Acetylethanolamine	60
Dimethylformamide	30
Formamide	30

The modification presented here can be applied to amides that form non-volatile amines because the titration medium is so designed to eliminate this form of interference.

Because the method is based upon an acid-base titration, materials that are not neutral to the indicator interfere. Compounds that react under the conditions of the method to consume potassium hydroxide also interfere. Esters and nitriles interfere in this respect, the former compounds quantitatively.

Hydroxamic Acid Colorimetric Method for Amides

Amides react with hydroxylamine to form the corresponding hydroxamic acids:

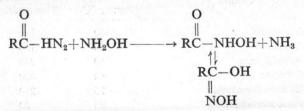

The hydroxamic acids formed can be determined colorimetrically by virtue of the colored complexes they form with ferric ion. The method of Bergmann[2] is described as follows.

Reagents. Hydroxylammonium sulfate, 2 N.
Sodium hydroxide, 3.5 N.
Hydrochloric acid, 3 N.
Ferric chloride, 0.74 M in 0.1 N hydrochloric acid.

Procedure. Mix equal volumes of the 2 N hydroxylammonium sulfate and 3.5 N sodium hydroxide. Pipet 2.0 ml. of the reagent into each of two 25-ml. glass-stoppered graduated cylinders. Reserve one of the cylinders as a blank. Pipet a 1.0 ml. aliquot (containing no more than 5 mmoles of amide) of the sample dilution into the other cylinder. React for the time and at the temperature specified in Table 11. Rapidly cool the contents of the cylinders to room temperature and add 1.0 ml. of the 3.5 N hydrochloric acid and 1.0 ml. of the 0.74 M ferric chloride. Immediately determine the absorbance of the sample vs. the blank at 540 mμ using 1 cm spectrophotometric cells. Note: The absorbance maximum may vary from compound to compound in which case the wave length of maximum absorption should be used.

Scope and Limitations. Most amides react to form hydroxamic acids; however, many of these compounds require long reaction times (see Table 11). Alkyl substituents on the nitrogen atom retard the rate of reaction, and compounds such as N-methylacetamide require several hours for complete reaction. Most of the iron complexes absorb in the region of 540 mμ; however, the absorption maximum for each complex should be determined for maximum sensitivity.

TABLE 11

REACTION CONDITIONS FOR DETERMINING AMIDES BY THE HYDROXAMIC ACID METHOD

Compound	Reaction Conditions	
	Temp., °C	Time, min.
Acetamide	60	120
Acetanilide	60	180
Acetylglycine	60	240
Caprolactam	60	420
Dimethylformamide	25	240
Fluoroacetamide	25	60
Formamide	25	60
N-Methylacetamide	60	420
Nicotinamide	25	480

The pH of the reaction mixture must be controlled fairly closely because free hydroxylamine (which is generated *in situ*) is required for the reaction and the amides may saponify under alkaline conditions.

Other carboxylic acid derivatives such as anhydrides, acid chlorides, imides, and esters undergo the same reaction and will interfere.

Any materials that react with hydroxylamine such as oxidizing agents or acylating reagents interfere by depleting the reagent.

MISCELLANEOUS

Reaction of Nitriles with Alkaline Hydrogen Peroxide

Nitriles are difficult to determine by chemical methods because of their lack of reactivity with common reagents. The method described below[14], which is based upon an alkaline reaction with hydrogen peroxide, is one of the few satisfactory methods for this class of compounds.

Nitriles react with alkaline hydrogen peroxide to form the corresponding amide. Under these conditions some of the amide is converted to the corresponding sodium salt. By concentrating the alkaline reagent, the remaining amide can be converted to the sodium salt. The excess potassium hydroxide is titrated with standard hydrochloric acid using phenophthalein indicator.

By suitable modification the procedure can be used for both macro concentrations and low (ppm) concentrations of nitrile in water. Both procedures are described below.

Reagents. Potassium hydroxide, 0.2 N and 1.0 N solutions.
Hydrogen peroxide, 3 and 30% reagent-grade solutions.
Hydrochloric acid, 0.1 N and 0.5 N standard solutions.
Phenolphthalein indicator, 1% solution in methanol.

Procedure. Macro Concentrations. Pipet 50.0 ml. of the 1 N potassium hydroxide into each of two 300-ml. 24/40 ⚶ glass-stoppered Corning alkali-resistant Erlenmeyer flasks. Pipet 100 ml. of 3% hydrogen peroxide into each flask. Reserve one of the flasks as a blank. Weigh 6 to 10 m-equiv. of nitrile into the other flask. Allow the flasks to stand at room temperature for 5 min. with occasional swirling. Add a few glass beads to each flask. Attach a 40 × 10 mm glass column, equipped with a 24/40 ⚶ ground-glass joint, to each flask. Apply heat and allow the contents of each flask to evaporate to approximately 10 ml. Cool and wash down each column with 100 ml. of water. Remove the column and pipet exactly 50.0 ml. of the 0.5 N hydrochloric acid into each flask. Titrate the contents of each flask with the standard 0.5 N hydrochloric acid using phenolphthalein indicator.

Low Concentrations in Water (5 to 1000 ppm). Pipet 25.0 ml. of the 0.2 N potassium hydroxide into each of two of the alkali-resistant flasks. Pipet 20 ml. of 30% hydrogen peroxide into each flask. Reserve one of the flasks as a blank. Pipet 200 ml. of the water sample into the other flask. Continue with the procedure above, except evaporate the contents of the flask to a volume of 2 ml. and titrate with 0.1 N hydrochloric acid.

Scope and Limitations. The alkaline hydrogen peroxide method has been applied to only a few nitriles including acetonitrile, propionitrile, butyronitrile, and succinonitrile. However, the method should be applicable to most simple aliphatic nitriles. The method is not applicable to acrylonitrile, benzonitrile, ethylene cyanohydrin, lactonitrile, and 3-methoxypropionitrile because side reactions give high results.

Compounds that oxidize to acids under the conditions of the method interfere. Some aldehydes interfere nearly quantitatively in this respect. Methanol, ethanol, and 2-propanol interfere only slightly and can be tolerated in small quantities. Esters and some amides interfere quantitatively in the method. Amines interfere with the indicator end point unless they are volatile under the evaporation conditions. Interference from amines that are non-volatile can be inhibited by incorporating pyridine in the titration medium.

Reduction of Aromatic Nitro Compounds with Stannous Chloride

The methods most commonly used for the determination of aromatic nitro compounds are based on the reduction to the corresponding amine with a suitable reducing agent:

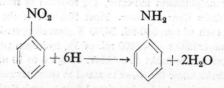

The method of Hinkel, Ayling, and Walters[6], which is presented here, is based upon the reduction with a measured excess of stannous chloride. After the reaction the excess reagent is titrated with standard iodine using starch indicator.

Reagents. Stannous chloride, 2.5 N in 3 N hydrochloric acid. Use water saturated with carbon dioxide for all dilutions.
Standard 0.6 N iodine solution.
Sulfuric acid, 50 v/v % aqueous solution.
Ethanol, carbonyl-free. Reflux for 3 to 4 hours while passing a stream of carbon dioxide through the solution.
Starch indicator.

Procedure. Connect a water-cooled condenser to a three-necked 250-ml. round-bottom flask. Seal a glass tube into one of the openings so that the tube will extend below the surface of the liquid. Connect the tube to a carbon dioxide cylinder and purge the equipment. Prepare duplicate equipment for a blank and sample determination. Stop the flow of carbon dioxide. Add 0.1 to 0.2 g of the nitro compound dissolved in 5 ml. of carbonyl-free ethanol into the sample flasks. Add 10 ml. of the 50% sulfuric acid to each flask. Pipet 10.0 ml. of the stannous chloride solution into each flask. Purge the solution with carbon dioxide at a rate of 2 bubbles sec. Heat the solution at 98°C for 90 minutes. If the nitro compound is insoluble and volatile, rinse the condensers with 2 ml. of the ethanol after 30 minutes and again after 60 minutes. Cool the flasks, maintaining the carbon dioxide purge, and add 200 ml. of water saturated with carbon dioxide. Titrate with the standard iodine solution using starch indicator.

Scope and Limitations. The stannous chloride method has been successfully applied to several types of aromatic nitro compounds including, mono-, di-, and tri-nitrohydrocarbons, nitrobenzaldehydes, nitroamines, nitrophenols, and nitro carboxylic acids.

Because stannous chloride is readily air oxidized, care must be taken to exclude oxygen during the analysis. Also the reagent should be protected from oxygen during storage.

Other compounds that can be reduced by stannous ion, such as aldehydes, azo and hydrazo compounds, and inorganic oxidizing agents, interfere.

Reaction of Isocyanates and Isothiocyanates with Butylamine

Organic isocyanates and isothiocyanates react with primary amines to form the corresponding ureas and thioureas:

$$1.\ RN{=}C{=}O + R'NH_2 \longrightarrow RN\overset{\overset{\displaystyle O}{\|}}{H}CNHR'$$

$$2.\ RN{=}C{=}S + R'NH_2 \longrightarrow RN\overset{\overset{\displaystyle S}{\|}}{H}CNHR'$$

This principle has been used by Siggia and Hanna[11] as the basis of a method for these compounds. In their method a measured excess of butylamine in dioxane is reacted with the sample. After the reaction is complete, the excess butylamine is titrated, in the presence of the weakly basic ureas, with standard sulfuric acid using methyl red indicator.

Reagents. Butylamine solution, 0.34 N in dry dioxane.
Standard 0.1 N sulfuric acid.
Methyl red indicator, 0.1 wt./vol. % aqueous solution.

Procedure. Pipet 20.0 ml. of the butylamine solution into each of two 250-ml. glass-stoppered Erlenmeyer flasks. Reserve one of the flasks as a blank. Weigh no more than 2 m-equiv. of isocyanate or isothiocyanate into the other flask. Allow the sample to react at room temperature for 45 min. Add 25 ml. of distilled water to each flask and titrate with the standard 0.1 N sulfuric acid using methyl red indicator.

Scope and Limitations. This method is applicable to phenyl and 1-naphthyl isocyanates, and methyl, ethyl, and phenyl isothiocyanates. Interferences in the method are restricted to acids and bases and materials that react with butylamine to form weaker bases. Corrections for acids and bases can usually be made independently. Anhydrides interfere by the formation of amides, while aldehydes may interfere via imine formation.

Colorimetric Determination of Quaternary Ammonium Compounds

Quaternary ammonium salts, that are surface-active, react with bromophenol blue in aqueous medium to form colored derivatives that are preferentially soluble in nonpolar media. The method of Auerbach[1], that follows, is based upon the spectrophotometric determination of the bromophenol blue derivatives.

Reagents. Bromophenol blue, 0.04% aqueous solution.
Sodium carbonate, 10% aqueous solution.
Ethylene dichloride.

Procedure. Prepare an aqueous dilution of the sample containing 0.1 mg/ml. of quaternary ammonium compound. Pipet 2.0 ml. of the dilution into a 125-ml. glass-stoppered separatory funnel. Add 2 ml. of the sodium carbonate solution and 1 ml. of the bromophenol blue solution. Pipet 10 ml. of the ethylene dichloride solution into the funnel, stopper, and shake the funnel gently for 1 min. Transfer the ethylene dichloride layer into a 1 cm spectrophotometric cell and determine the absorbance at the point of maximum absorption using ethylene dichloride as a blank. Determine the concentration of quaternary ammonium compound from a calibration curve obtained with the compound being determined.

Scope and Limitations. The bromophenol blue method can be used to determine quaternary ammonium compounds that contain at least 8–10 carbon atoms. Compounds with fewer carbon atoms do not form the organic soluble derivatives. Some representative type compounds that can be determined include the alkyl pyridinium and the trialkyl benzylammonium halides.

Although the method may not be completely specific, the only interferences known are due to colored compounds that extract into ethylene dichloride from water. Corrections can be made for such interferences.

REFERENCES

1 AUERBACH, M. E., *Ind. Eng. Chem., Anal. Ed.*, 15, 492 (1943).
2. BERGMANN, F., *Anal. Chem.*, 24, 1367 (1952).
3. CRITCHFIELD, F. E., JOHNSON, J. B., *Anal. Chem.* 28, 430 (1956).
4. CRITCHFIELD, F. E., JOHNSON, J. B., *Anal. Chem.* 436 (1956).
5. CRITCHFIELD, F. E., JOHNSON, J. B., *Anal. Chem.* 29, 1174 (1957).
6. HINKEL, L. E., AYLING, E. E., WALTERS, T. M., *J. Chem. Soc.*, 1939, 403.
7. MIZUCH, K. G., SAVCHENKO, A. Y., *Org. Chem. Ind. U.S.S.R.*, 7, 24 (1940).
8. OLSEN, S., *Chemie*, 56, 202 (1943).
9. PIFER, C. W., WOLLISH, E. B., *Anal. Chem.*, 24, 300 (1952).
10. RUCH, J. E., CRITCHFIELD, F. E., *Anal. Chem.* 33, 1569 (1961).
11. SIGGIA, S., HANNA, J. G., *Ind. Eng. Chem., Anal. Ed.*, 20, 1084 (1948).
12. SIGGIA, S., HANNA, J. G., KERVENSKI, I. R., *Anal. Chem.*, 22, 1295 (1950).
13. WAGNER, C. O., BROWN, R. H., PETERS, E. D., *J. Amer. Chem. Soc.*, 69, 2611 (1947).
14. WHITEHURST. D. H., JOHNSON, J. B., *Anal. Chem.*, 30, 1332 (1958).
15. WOELFEL, W. C., *Anal. Chem.* 20, 722 (1948).

CHAPTER 4

CARBONYL COMPOUNDS AND DERIVATIVES

ALDEHYDES and ketones can be determined by a large number of methods that are based upon the reaction of the carbonyl group, $C=O$. Derivatives of aldehydes and ketones, including acetals,

$$R-C\begin{smallmatrix}H \\ \diagup \\ \diagdown\end{smallmatrix}\begin{smallmatrix}OR' \\ \\ OR'\end{smallmatrix}, \text{ketals}, \begin{smallmatrix}R' \\ \diagdown \\ \diagup \\ R'\end{smallmatrix}C\begin{smallmatrix}OR'' \\ \\ OR''\end{smallmatrix}, \text{and imines}, R-C\begin{smallmatrix}H \\ \| \\ \end{smallmatrix}=N-R',$$

can also be determined by some of these methods provided that the derivative can be hydrolyzed to the parent carbonyl compound under the conditions of the analysis.

The more generally applicable methods for carbonyl compounds are based upon the reaction with hydroxylamine to form the corresponding oxime:

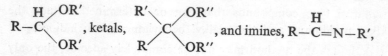

$$\begin{smallmatrix}R \\ \diagdown \\ \diagup \\ R\end{smallmatrix}C=O + NH_2OH \longrightarrow \begin{smallmatrix}R \\ \diagdown \\ \diagup \\ R\end{smallmatrix}C=N-OH + H_2O$$

Because free hydroxylamine is relatively unstable to air oxidation, it is almost invariably used as the salt. The two salts most successfully used are hydroxylamine hydrochloride[2,3] and the corresponding formate[6,9].

When the oximation reaction is conducted with hydroxylamine hydrochloride, the following equilibrium reaction is obtained:

$$\begin{smallmatrix}R \\ \diagdown \\ \diagup \\ R\end{smallmatrix}C=O + NH_2OH \cdot HCl \rightleftharpoons \begin{smallmatrix}R \\ \diagdown \\ \diagup \\ R\end{smallmatrix}C=N-OH + HCl + H_2O$$

In order to obtain quantitative reaction, the system must be buffered by the addition of bases so that the solution does not become so acidic that the oxime is hydrolyzed to the free carbonyl[2]. Bases that are successfully employed include triethanolamine[3] and dimethylethanolamine[4].

Various combinations of solvent systems, hydroxylamine salts, and bases (proton acceptors) are used to prevent hydrolysis of carbonyl derivatives, or to obtain quantitative hydrolysis of these derivatives, and to obtain more precise results via sharper end points.

In some cases, aldehydes must be determined in the presence of ketones and/or other carbonyl derivatives. Methods available for such determinations are usually based upon the relative ease of oxidation of the aldehydic carbonyl group to the corresponding acid. One particularly valuable method[8] is based upon the oxidation by potassium mercuric iodide ("mercural" reagent).

Low concentrations of carbonyl compounds are more conveniently determined by colorimetric methods than by titrimetric procedures. The colorimetric reagent most generally used for aldehydes, ketones, and their derivatives is 2,4-dinitrophenylhydrazine[1,5,7].

HYDROXYLAMINE HYDROCHLORIDE-TRIETHANOL-AMINE METHODS

Aldehydes and Ketones

The most common method for determining aldehydes and ketones is based upon the reaction with hydroxylamine hydrochloride in the presence of a base. In the procedure described here, triethanolamine is used to convert the hydrochloride, in part, to free hydroxylamine[3]:

$$NH_2OH \cdot HCl + (HOCH_2CH_2)_3N \rightarrow NH_2OH + (HOCH_2CH_2)_3N \cdot HCl$$

The free hydroxylamine reacts with the aldehyde or ketone to form the oxime:

$$\overset{H}{RC}=O + NH_2OH \longrightarrow \overset{H}{RC}=NOH + H_2O$$

The amount of hydroxylamine consumed, which is measured by titration of the excess base with standard acid, is a measure of the carbonyl compound present in the sample.

Although the end point in this method leaves something to be desired, the method is readily adaptable to the determination of the derivatives of carbonyl compounds and is included for this reason.

Reagents. 2-Propanol, containing not more than 0.05 per cent carbonyl compounds as acetone.

0.5 N Hydroxylamine hydrochloride. Dissolve the hydroxylamine hydrochloride in 150 ml. of distilled water and dilute to 1 liter with the 2-propanol.

Bromophenol blue indicator, 0.04 per cent solution in 2-propanol.

0.5 N Aqueous triethanolamine.

Standard 0.5 N aqueous hydrochloric acid.

Procedure. Add 30 ml. of the bromophenol blue indicator to 1 l. of the hydroxylamine hydrochloride reagent. Neutralize the solution with the 0.5 N triethanolamine. Prepare fresh solution each day. Add 65 ml. of the neutralized hydroxylamine hydrochloride solution from a graduated cylinder, to each of two heat-resistant pressure bottles (for reactions at room temperature glass-stoppered Erlenmeyer flasks can also be used). Pipet 50 ml. of the triethanolamine solution into each bottle. Purge the bottles with nitrogen and cap until the sample is introduced. Accurately weigh no more than 12.5 m-equiv. of the carbonyl compound into one of the bottles and cap the bottle. If the reaction is at 98°C, insert the bottles in fabric bags and place them in a steam bath for sufficient time to obtain quantitative reaction. Refer to Table 12 for the reaction conditions for several carbonyl compounds. When the reaction is complete, remove the bottles from the bath and cool them to room temperature. Uncap the bottles carefully to release any pressure and remove the bags. Titrate the blank with the standard hydrochloric acid to a greenish-blue end point. Titrate the sample to a color matching that of the blank.

Scope and Limitations. The hydroxylamine hydrochloride-triethanolamine method has been applied to a large number of aldehydes and ketones, a few of which are shown in Table 12. Most carbonyl compounds react quantitatively with the reagent; however, elevated temperatures are required for the less reactive compounds, particularly the higher molecular weight carbonyls and sterically hindered compounds.

Because the reaction medium used in the method is roughly 50 per cent water, difficulty may be experienced with water inso-

luble compounds. This can be overcome by using 2-propanol
as a cosolvent. When a cosolvent is used for the sample the
same volume should be added to the blank.

Because the end point of the titration of hydroxylamine is
buffered by the oxime (see Fig. 12), this method is not as

TABLE 12

REACTION CONDITIONS FOR CARBONYL COMPOUNDS BY THE HYDRO-
XYLAMINE HYDROCHLORIDE-TRIETHANOLAMINE METHOD

Compound	Reaction Conditions		Number of Reacting Groups
	Time, min.	Temp °C	
Acetaldehyde	30	25	1
Acetone	30	25	1
Acetonylacetone	120	25	2
Acetophenone	60	98	1
Benzaldehyde	15	25	1
Crotonaldehyde	30	25	1
Diisobutyl ketone	120	98	1
2-Ethylhexaldehyde	60	98	1
Formaldehyde	15	25	1
Glyoxal	15	25	2
Hexaldehyde	60	98	1
α-Methylglutaraldehyde	15	98	2
Mesityl oxide	45	98	1
Octylaldehyde	60	25	1
Propionaldehyde	30	25	1

precise as other methods that will be presented. If the color of
the indicator in the blank and the sample are carefully matched
at the end point, results within ± 0.5 per cent can be obtained
or most compounds.

Strong inorganic acids and bases and most aliphatic amines
will interfere quantitatively and can be corrected for. Serious
interference is obtained from organic acids since they are not
quantitatively acidic to the bromophenol blue indicator. Samples
that contain low concentrations of organic acids (less than 0.5
m-equiv.) can be neutralized to the indicator before the addition
of the reagent and can be successfully analyzed. Although large
concentrations of inert solvents can be tolerated, they tend to

affect the color of the indicator at the end point, and cause difficulty in matching the color of the sample to that of the blank. Compounds that acid-hydrolyze to aldehydes and ketones, such as acetals, ketals, vinyl ethers, and vinyl esters interfere

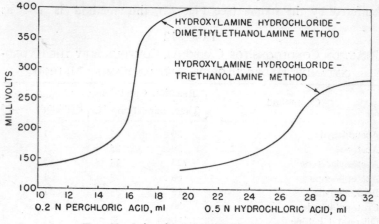

FIG. 12. Oximation of methyl isobutyl ketone

in the method. When compounds such as these are present, a modification of this method, presented subsequently, should be used to determine total carbonyl and a more specific method should be used for free carbonyl.

Acetals, Ketals, and Vinyl Alkyl Ethers

Derivatives of carbonyl compounds that acid-hydrolyze to aldehydes and ketones can be determined readily by a modification of the hydroxylamine hydrochloride-triethanolamine method. Acetals, ketals, and vinyl alkyl ethers hydrolyze to carbonyl compounds in the following manner:

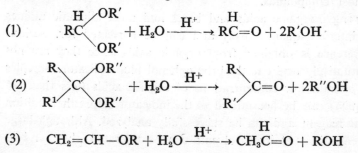

(1) $$RC\!\!\begin{array}{c} H \\ OR' \\ OR' \end{array} + H_2O \xrightarrow{H^+} RC\!\!=\!\!O + 2R'OH$$

(2) $$\begin{array}{c} R \\ R^1 \end{array}\!\!C\!\!\begin{array}{c} OR'' \\ OR'' \end{array} + H_2O \xrightarrow{H^+} \begin{array}{c} R \\ R' \end{array}\!\!C\!\!=\!\!O + 2R''OH$$

(3) $$CH_2\!\!=\!\!CH\!-\!OR + H_2O \xrightarrow{H^+} CH_3C\!\!=\!\!O + ROH$$

These carbonyl derivatives can be hydrolyzed in an acidified solution of hydroxylamine hydrochloride. Under these conditions the hydrolysis occurs readily, being aided by the oximation of the free carbonyl compound as it is formed. When the hydrolysis reaction is complete, triethanolamine is added to increase the pH of the solution so that the oximation reaction will also be quantitative. The titration and most other aspects of the method are similar to the method for free carbonyl compounds.

Reagents. The reagents used in this method are the same as in the corresponding method for aldehydes and ketones.

Procedure. Add 30 ml. of bromophenol blue indicator to 1 l. of the 0.5 N hydroxylamine hydrochloride. Neutralize the solution with 0.5 N triethanolamine. Prepare fresh solution each day. Add 50 ml. of the neutralized hydroxylamine hydrochloride solution from a graduated cylinder, to each of two heat-resistant pressure bottles (for reactions at room temperature glass-stoppered Erlenmeyer flasks can also be used). Pipet 1.0 ml. of 0.5 N hydrochloric acid into each bottle. Purge the bottles with nitrogen and cap until the sample is introduced. Accurately weigh no more than 12.5 m-equiv. of carbonyl derivative into one of the bottles and cap the bottle. Add 2-propanol as a co-solvent to both the blank and sample if required (refer to Table 13). If elevated temperatures are required, insert the bottles in fabric bags and place them in a steam bath at $98 \pm 2°C$ for sufficient time to obtain quantitative reaction. Refer to Table 13 for the reaction conditions for several carbonyl derivatives. When the reaction is complete, remove the bottles from the bath and cool them to room temperature. Uncap the bottles carefully to release any pressure and remove the bags. Pipet 50.0 ml. of 0.5 N triethanolamine into each bottle and allow the bottles to stand for 15 minutes. Titrate the blank with the standard 0.5 N hydrochloric acid to a greenish-blue end point. Titrate the sample to a color matching that of the blank.

Scope and Limitations. The hydroxylamine hydrochloride-triethanolamine method, previously described, is ideally suited for determining most acetals, ketals, and vinyl ethers since the reagent contains approximately 50 per cent water, and the addition of a small amount of acid is all that is required for quantitative hydrolysis. The method has been applied to a large number of these carbonyl derivatives, a few of which are shown in Table 13. The method is not applicable to the determination of certain formals, polymers of formaldehyde, and certain cyclic acetal derivatives of ethylene glycol, because the reaction medium is insufficiently acidic for quantitative hydrolysis. Vinyl alkyl esters consume more than one mole of hydroxylamine because organic acids are products of the hydrolysis:

$$R-\overset{\overset{\displaystyle O}{\|}}{C}-OCH=CH_2 + H_2O \xrightarrow{\ H^+\ } R\overset{\overset{\displaystyle O}{\|}}{C}-OH + CH_3\overset{\overset{\displaystyle H}{}}{C}=O$$

The organic acids are not quantitatively acidic to bromophenol blue indicator; therefore, less than stoichiometric results are obtained.

TABLE 13

REACTION CONDITIONS FOR ACETALS, KETALS, AND VINYL ALKYL ETHERS BY THE ACIDIC HYDROXYLAMINE HYDROCHLORIDE-TRIETHANOLAMINE METHOD

Compound	2-Propanol, ml.	Reaction Conditions	
		Time, min.	Temp. °C
Acetals and Ketals			
Diallyl acetal	0	15	98
Diallyl ketal	0	15	25
Dibutyl acetal	0	30	25
Diethyl acetal	0	15	25
Di(2-ethylhexyl) 2-ethylhexanal	50	15	98
Diethyl ketal	0	15	25
Dimethyl butyral	0	15	98
Vinyl Alkyl Ethers			
Isopropenyl ethyl ether	0	15	25
Vinyl allyl ether	25	30	98
Vinyl butyl ether	50	20	25
Vinyl 2-chloroethyl ether	25	30	98
Vinyl ethyl ether	0	180	25
Vinyl methyl ether	0	60	25

Most aldehydes and ketones also react quantitatively under the conditions of this method; therefore, the procedure can be used for determining both free and combined carbonyl. When used in conjunction with a specific method for carbonyl compounds, the procedure can be used to resolve mixtures of carbonyl compounds and their derivatives.

Conventional hydroxylamine methods can not be used exclusively in nonaqueous media, because of the insolubility of the hydrochloride salts of the bases used to neutralize part of the hydroxylamine hydrochloride. In the method of Fritz, dimethylethanolamine is used as the base and forms a hydrochloride that is soluble in the nonaqueous media. Improved precision is also aided by using perchloric acid in methyl Cellosolve as the titrant. The procedure presented here is a modification of the original procedure of Fritz and coworkers [4].

Reagents. 0.4 N Hydroxylamine hydrochloride. Dissolve hydroxylamine hydrochloride in 300 ml. of methanol and dilute to 1 l. with 2-propanol.

0.25 M Dimethylethanolamine in 2-propanol.

0.1 M Perchloric acid in methyl Cellosolve. Prepare the solution from 70 to 72 per cent perchloric acid and standardize against tris (hydroxymethyl) aminomethane (Fisher's certified reagent) in water using bromocresol green indicator.

Martius yellow–methyl violet mixed indicator. Dissolve 0.13 g of martius yellow and 0.008 g of methyl violet in 100 ml. of ethanol.

Procedure. Pipet 20.0 ml. of 0.25 M dimethylethanolamine into each of two glass-stoppered Erlenmeyer flasks. Pipet 25.0 ml. of 0.4 M hydroxylamine hydrochloride into each flask. Accurately weigh no more than 2.5m-equiv. of carbonyl compound into one of the flasks. Stopper the flasks and allow them to stand for sufficient time to give quantitative reaction. See Table 15 for the reaction conditions for several carbonyl compounds. Add 5 drops of the mixed indicator and titrate the contents of each flask with the standard perchloric acid to a colorless end point.

Scope and Limitations. The main advantage this method has over conventional hydroxylamine methods is the precision which can be obtained because of the well-defined end point. The curves in Fig. 12 show a comparison of this method with the hydroxylamine hydrochloride-triethanolamine method. As mentioned previously, the enhancement of the potentiometric end point is brought about by using a nonaqueous medium and perchloric acid titrant. Because of the sharp end point a precision of ± 0.1 per cent can be obtained by this method.

Since a nonaqueous medium is used in this method, less interference is encountered from organic acids than in the conventional hydroxylamine method. Fritz obtained no interference from benzoic acid when present in an equimolar mixture with vanillin; however, a buffered end point was obtained when the ratio was 5 to 1.

Less interference is obtained from acetals, ketals, and vinyl ethers in this method than in the hydroxylamine hydrochloride-triethanolamine method, because of the nonaqueous medium. However, interference can be encountered, particularly from ketals, because of traces of water in the reagents and because of the very strong acid used as the titrant. This method cannot be readily modified to determine acetals, ketals, and vinyl ethers quantitatively. When sufficient water and excess acid are added to effect the hydrolysis, the end point is considerably buffered and the indicator end point does not coincide with the potentiometric break.

TABLE 15

REACTION CONDITIONS FOR DETERMINING CARBONYL
COMPOUNDS BY THE HYDROXYLAMINE
HYDROCHLORIDE-DIMETHYLETHANOLAMINE METHOD

Compound	Reaction Time, min at 25°C
Acetone	30 [a]
Acetophenone	30 [b]
Benzaldehyde	20
Butyraldehyde	20
Cyclohexanone	30
Cyclopentanone	30
Formaldehyde	210 [a]
Furfural	20
p-Hydroxybenzaldehyde	5
Methyl ethyl ketone	30 [a]
Methyl isobutyl ketone	30
p-Nitrobenzaldehyde	20
Salicylaldehyde	5
Tridecanone	5

[a] Data by author, all other data by Fritz and coworkers [4].
[b] Minutes at 70°C.

Most carbonyl compounds react quantitatively with the reagent at room temperature; although, aromatic ketones and sterically hindered carbonyl compounds usually require elevated temperatures for quantitative reaction (see Table 15). When elevated temperatures are required, temperatures in excess of 70°C are not recommended because of excessive instability of the reagent.

HYDROXYLAMMONIUM FORMATE

None of the previously described hydroxylamine methods is particularly adaptable to the determination of carbonyl compounds in the presence of acetals, ketals, and vinyl ethers. The hydroxylammonium formate method presented here, which is a modification[9] of the original procedure of Pesez[6], fulfills this important need.

In methyl Cellosolve medium, hydroxylammonium formate reacts with carbonyl compounds in the following manner:

$$\begin{array}{c} R \\ \diagdown \\ C=O + NH_2OH \cdot HCOOH \rightarrow \\ \diagup \\ R \end{array} \quad \begin{array}{c} R \\ \diagdown \\ C=NOH + HCOOH + H_2O \\ \diagup \\ R \end{array}$$

The excess hydroxylamine is titrated with standard nitric acid in methyl Cellosolve using thymol blue indicator. In the non-aqueous medium used, formic acid and the oximes are neutral to the indicator. Separate procedures are presented in the following sections for determining macro and low concentrations of carbonyl compounds:

Reagents. 0.5 N Hydroxylammonium formate in methyl Cellosolve. Add 6.5 g of reagent-grade potassium hydroxide pellets to 70 ml. of methyl Cellosolve contained in a 400-ml. beaker. Add 4 ml. of concentrated formic acid and stir until the pellets are dissolved. Neutralize the solution to phenolphthalein indicator with formic acid, then add one more pellet of potassium hydroxide and dissolve. Prepare a second solution by dissolving 6.8 g of hydroxylamine hydrochloride in 130 ml. of methyl Cellosolve. Mix the two solutions, cool to 15°C. and filter to remove the precipitated potassium chloride. This reagent is stable for at least 2 weeks, but should be discarded when the blank titration is less than 35 ml.

0.1 N Hydroxylammonium formate. Dilute the 0.5 N reagent with carbonyl-free methanol (see p. 78). This solution is also stable for 2 weeks but should be discarded when the blank is less than 20 ml.

0.5 N Nitric acid in methyl Cellosolve. Prepare from concentrated nitric acid and inhibit the solution against peroxide formation by adding 1.0 g of urea and 0.1 g of p-diethoxybenzene to 1 l. of the solution. Standardize the solution against tris (hydroxymethyl) aminomethane (Fischer's certified reagent) dissolved in 50 ml. of methanol and 100 ml. of propylene glycol, using thymol blue indicator.

0.02 N Nitric acid. Prepare by making an accurate dilution of the 0.5 N reagent with carbonyl-free methanol. No further standardization is necessary.

Thymol blue indicator, 0.3 per cent solution in dimethylformamide.

Procedure for macro concentrations. Pipet 50.0 ml. of 0.5 N hydroxylammonium formate into each of two glass-stoppered Erlenmeyer flasks. Accurately weigh no more than 15 m-equiv. of carbonyl compound into one of the flasks. Allow the sample to react for sufficient time to obtain quantitative reaction. Refer to Table 16 for the reaction conditions for several carbonyl compounds. Add 50 ml. of methanol, 75 ml. of methyl Cellosolve, and 5 or 6 drops of thymol blue indicator to each flask. Titrate to a definite orange color using the standard 0.5 N nitric acid.

Procedure for low concentrations. Pipet exactly 5,0 ml. of the 0.1 N hydroxylammonium formate into each of two glass-stoppered Erlenmeyer flasks. Accurately weigh or pipet no more than 0.3 meq of carbonyl compound into one of the flasks. The total volume of sample added should not exceed 10 ml. Allow the sample to react for sufficient time to obtain quantitative reaction. Refer to Table 17 for the reaction conditions for several carbonyl compounds. Add 3 drops of the thymol blue indicator and titrate with the standard 0.02 N nitric acid to a definite orange color. Match the color of the sample to that of the blank at the end point.

Scope in Limitations. Although the precision of the hydroxylammonium formate method is not as good as the hydroxylamine hydrochloride-dimethylethanolamine method, it is superior to conventional hydroxylamine methods. Figure 13 shows potentiometric titration curves obtained by this method and the hydroxylamine hydrochloride-triethanolamine method. Because of the somewhat enhanced potentiometric break, this method is capable of a precision of ± 0.2 per cent for refined materials.

The macro method has been applied to a wide variety of carbonyl compounds and the reaction conditions for several of

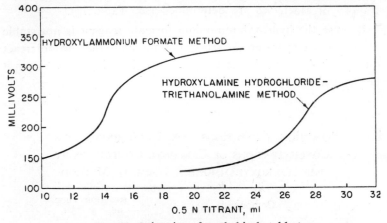

FIG. 13. Oximation of methyl isobutyl ketone

these are given in Table 16. Ketones tend to react more readily than the low molecular weight aldehydes, presumably because

TABLE 16

REACTION CONDITIONS FOR DETERMINING MACRO
CONCENTRATIONS OF CARBONYL COMPOUNDS BY
THE HYDROXYLAMMONIUM FORMATE METHOD

Compound	Reaction Time, min. at 25°C
Acetaldehyde	15 [a]
Acetone	15
Butyraldehyde	15
Crotonaldehyde	15
Ethyl butyl ketone	15
2-Ethylbutyraldehyde	15
2-Ethylhexaldehyde	30
Formaldehyde	120
2,4-Hexadienal	15
Methyl ethyl ketone	15
Methyl isobutyl ketone	15
Propionaldehyde	60 [a]

[a] For refined material, use a dilution in methyl Cellosolve to prevent evaporation losses.

of the tendency of the aldehydes to form hemiacetals with the solvent. This effect is particularly noticable when low concentrations of aldehydes are determined (see Table 17).

Because the hydroxylammonium formate reagent is not stable at elevated temperatures, carbonyl compounds that do not react quantitatively at moderate temperatures (less than 50°C) cannot be determined by the method.

TABLE 17

REACTION CONDITIONS FOR DETERMINING LOW
CONCENTRATIONS OF CARBONYL COMPOUNDS BY
THE HYDROXYLAMMONIUM FORMATE METHOD

Compound	Reaction Time, min. at 25°C
Acetone	15
Butyraldehyde	30
2-Ethylbutyraldehyde	90
Formaldehyde	240
Glyoxal	30

This method is particularly advantageous for determining carbonyl compounds in the presence of acetals, ketals, and vinyl ethers. Even the more reactive ketals, such as dimethoxypropane, do not interfere in the method. Interference from these readily hydrolyzable compounds does not occur because the reaction medium is nonaqueous, and because the relatively weak mineral acid, nitric, is used as the titrant. When the considerably stronger acid, perchloric, is substituted in the method, the potentiometric end point is considerably sharper, but interference from carbonyl derivatives is excessive. The method is useful in conjunction with the acidic hydroxylamine hydrochloride-triethanolamine procedure for resolving mixtures of free and combined carbonyl.

When the procedure is used for low concentrations, most carbonyl compounds can be determined in concentrations as low as 50 ppm without interference from hydrolyzable carbonyl derivatives.

Most inorganic bases and aliphatic amines interfere quantitatively in the method and can be corrected for. Acids with ionization constants greater than 1×10^{-2} interfere. Most organic, acids do not interfere appreciably. Large quantities of water (more than 20 per cent in the reaction mixture) interfere particularly when acetals, ketals, and vinyl ethers are present.

MERCURIMETRIC DETERMINATION OF ALDEHYDES

A common problem in organic analysis is the analytical resolution of mixtures containing both aldehydes and ketones. The most satisfactory method of performing this analysis is to determine the aldehyde specifically by the mercurimetric oxidation method described here [8] and to determine the total carbonyl by one of the hydroxylamine procedures.

In the presence of an alkaline solution of potassium mercuric iodide of definite composition (called "mercural" reagent to differentiate it from Nessler's reagent), aldehydes are oxidized to the corresponding acid, effecting a quantitative liberation of mercury:

$$RCHO + Hg^{++} + 2OH^- \longrightarrow RCOOH + Hg + H_2O$$

The reduced mercury is maintained in a finely-divided state by using an agar solution as a protective colloid. The reaction mixture is acidified and the mercury is reacted with a measured excess of iodine:

$$Hg + I_2 \longrightarrow HgI_2$$

The amount of iodine consumed, which is determined by titration of the excess with standard sodium thiosulfate, is a measure of the aldehyde oxidized.

Reagents. Mercural reagent. Dissolve 150 g of reagent-grade potassium chloride, 240 g of USP-grade mercuric chloride, and 642 g of reagent-grade potassium iodide in 1830 ml. of distilled water. Add 1 l. of 40 per cent potassium hydroxide and mix the solution. The reagent is stable and is not affected by the yellow or brown precipitate that may form on standing.

Agar solution, 0.1 per cent. Dissolve 3.0 g of Difco Bacto-Agar in 300 ml. of boiling water. Continue heating until the solution is essentially clear. Dilute to 3 l. with distilled water and add 0.1 g of mercuric iodide as a preservative.

Acetic acid, Grasselli grade or equivalent.
Iodine, approximately 0.1 N.
Standard 0.1 N sodium thiosulfate.
Starch indicator, 0.1 per cent.

Procedure. Add 50 ml. of mercural reagent to each of two 500-ml. iodine flasks. If the reaction is to be conducted at 0°C, (see Table 18), cool the flasks in an ice bath for 10 min. Accurately add no more than 3.0 m-equiv. of aldehyde into one of the flasks. An aliquot of a dilution is normally used (see Table 18) and the same volume of solvent should be added to the blank. Allow the sample to react for sufficient time to obtain quantitative reaction. Reaction conditions for several aldehydes are listed in Table 18. Add 50 ml. of agar solution to each flask and mix to disperse the precipitated mercury. Add 25 ml. of acetic acid and immediately pipet 50.0 ml. of 0.1 N iodine into each flask. For acetaldehyde, allow 15 minutes between the addition of acetic acid and iodine. Stopper the flasks and shake them vigorously until the mercury is completely dissolved. Remove the stoppers and rinse the walls of the flasks with distilled water. Titrate the contents of each flask with standard 0.1 N sodium thiosulfate using starch indicator.

Scope and Limitations. The mercural method can be used to determine aldehydes specifically in the presence of a wide variety of materials. Several of the aldehydes that have been determined by the method are listed in Table 18. The method is particularly valuable for determining aldehydes in the presence of ketones.

The standard deviation of the method for determining the purity of acetaldehyde is 0.39 per cent. With slight modification, the method can also be used to determine ppm concentrations of aldehydes. When a 20 g sample is used, as little as 50 ppm acetaldehyde can readily be determined.

Ketones are not oxidized by the reagent but a side-reaction with acetone can be a source of difficulty. Acetone reacts with mercuric ion to form an insoluble complex:

$$Hg^{++} + 2CH_3\text{-}\overset{\overset{\displaystyle O}{\|}}{C}\text{-}CH_3 \rightleftharpoons Hg\,(CH_3\text{-}\overset{\overset{\displaystyle \bar{O}}{|}}{C}{=}CH_2)_2 + 2H^+$$

In the presence of the alkaline reagent and excess of mercuric ion, the formation of the insoluble complex is favored. When the reagent is acidified, the complex dissolves. The reversal of the reaction must be complete or else iodine will be consumed by reaction with the complex. No appreciable difficulty is experienced in the presence of acetone with aldehydes that are oxidized at 25°C. However, if the reaction is conducted at 0°C, only 0.3 g of acetone can be tolerated. Methyl ethyl ketone complexes mercury to a much smaller degree than acetone, while

TABLE 18

REACTION CONDITIONS FOR DETERMINING ALDEHYDES BY MERCURIMETRIC OXIDATION

Compound	Dilution Solvent [a]	Reaction Conditions	
		Temp., °C	Time, min.
Acetaldehyde	water	25	5
Acetaldol	water	0	5
Acrolein	methanol	0	180
Benzaldehyde	methanol	0	15
Butyraldehyde	water	25	15
2-Ethylhexaldehyde	[b]	0	120
Formaldehyde	water	25	5
Glutaraldehyde	water	25	5
Hexaldehyde	[c]	25	30
Methacrolein	methanol	0	15
Propionaldehyde	water	25	15

[a] If methanol is specified, neutralize the solvent to bromothymol blue indicator prior to use.

[b] Weigh the sample directly into the flask and add 25 ml. of methanol co-solvent to both the sample and blank flasks.

[c] Weigh the sample directly into the sample flask and place the flask on a shaker for the time specified above.

methyl isopropyl ketone and ethyl butyl ketone do not interfere at all.

Hydroxy ketones interfere as do other easily oxidized substances or compounds that consume iodine. Oxidizing agents, such as peroxides, produce low results.

Some vinyl compounds interfere by adding iodine. Although the method has been applied to the determination of acrolein and methacrolein, unsaturated aldehydes containing more than four carbon atoms cannot be determined.

Acids and esters do not interfere if no more than one-third of the potassium hydroxide in the reagent is consumed.

2,4-DINITROPHENYLHYDRAZINE COLORIMETRIC METHOD

Although some of the methods previously described can be used to determine low concentrations of aldehydes and/or ketones, colorimetric procedures are generally more sensitive than titrimetric methods.

2,4-Dinitrophenylhydrazine is the most commonly used reagent for determining carbonyl compounds and several methods based upon the reagent have been presented [1,5]. The modification[7] described here is based upon the reaction of the carbonyl compound to form the corresponding hydrazone:

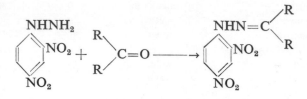

Potassium hydroxide is then added to produce a wine-red color, presumably due to a resonating quinoidal ion:

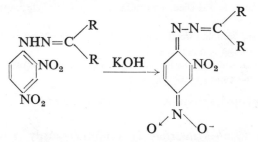

The color is measured spectrophotometrically at 480 mμ.

Reagents. Carbonyl-free methanol. Distill 3 gal of methanol from a mixture containing 50 g of 2,4-dinitrophenylhydrazine and 15 ml. of concentrated hydrochloric acid. Reflux for 4 hours and collect the fraction boiling to 64.8°C.

Pyridine, redistilled. Store over potassium hydroxide pellets. Pyridine stabilizer, 80:20 v/v % pyridine-water solution.

2,4-Dinitrophenylhydrazine solution. Add 50 mg of reagent-grade 2,4-dinitrophenylhydrazine to 25 ml. of carbonyl-free methanol. Add 2 ml. of concentrated hydrochloric acid and dilute to 50 ml. with distilled water. The reagent is stable for 2 weeks.

Potassium hydroxide in carbonyl-free methanol, 33%.

Procedure. Prepare a 100 ml. dilution of the sample, containing no more than 40 μmoles of carbonyl compounds, in carbonyl-free methanol. Pipet 2 ml. of the sample dilution into one of two 25-ml. glass-stoppered graduated cylinders. Add 2 ml. of carbonyl-free methanol to the other cylinder and process as a blank. Pipet 2 ml. of the 2,4-dinitrophenylhydrazine reagent into each cylinder, mix and allow to react for 30 min. Pipet 10 ml. of the pyridine stabilizer into each cylinder. Pipet 2 ml. of the potassium hydroxide solution into each cylinder and mix. Obtain the absorbance of the sample vs. the blank at 480 mμ, using 1 cm cells, within 10±1 min after the addition of the potassium hydroxide solution. Determine the concentration of carbonyl compound by reference to a calibration curve.

Scope and Limitations. Because the intensity of the color reaction for most carbonyl compounds is independent of the nature of the compound, most aldehydes and ketones give colors proportional to their molecular weights. Therefore, separate calibration curves are not necessary for each carbonyl compound determined. Exceptions to this include α,β-unsaturated carbonyl compounds, such as crotonaldehyde and 2,4-hexadienal, and bifunctional carbonyl compounds like glyoxal and benzoquinone. In each of these cases, increased conjugation from the hydrazone structure contributes to the color intensity of the quinoidal ion.

Acetals, ketals, vinyl ethers, and imines hydrolyze under the conditions of the reaction with 2,4-dinitrophenylhydrazine and can be determined by this method. The method is therefore valuable for determining low concentrations of free and combined carbonyl in the presence of most organic compounds. Interferences in the method are generally restricted to materials that consume 2,4-dinitrophenylhydrazine such as oxidizing agents, epoxides, and anhydrides.

SUMMARY

The hydroxylamine hydrochloride-triethanolamine method is applicable to a wide variety of carbonyl compounds and can be modified for the determination of acetals, ketals, vinyl ethers, and imines. When a high degree of precision is required, particularly in the determination of high-purity materials, the hydroxylamine hydrochloride-dimethylethanolamine method should be used. The hydroxylammonium formate method provides a means of determining carbonyl compounds without interference from compounds that acid-hydrolyze to aldehydes or ketones. Mixtures of aldehydes and ketones can be resolved by determining the aldehyde specifically using the "mercural" method. Although the hydroxylammonium formate method can be adapted to the determination of low concentrations of carbonyl compounds and the mercural method to the similar determination of aldehydes, the colorimetric 2,4-dinitrophenylhydrazine method is more sensitive, though less specific.

REFERENCES

1. BOHME, H., WINKLER, O., Z. Anal. Chem., **142**, 1 (1954).
2. BRYANT, W. M. D., SMITH, D. M., J. Amer. Chem. Soc., **57**, 57 (1935).
3. FUNK, G. L., unpublished data, Union Carbide Chemicals Co., South Charleston, W. Va.
4. FRITZ, J. S., YAMAMURA, S S., BRADFORD, E. C., Anal. Chem. **31**, 260 (1959).
5. LAPPIN, G. R., CLARK, L. C., Anal. Chem., **23**, 541 (1951).
6. PESEZ, M., Bull. soc. Chim. France. **1957**, 417.
7. ROHRBOUGH, W. G., unpublished data, Union Carbide Chemicals Co. South Charleston, W. Va.
8. RUCH, J. E., JOHNSON, J. B., Anal. Chem., **28**, 69 (1956).
9. RUCH, J. E., JOHNSON, J. B., CRITCHFIELD, F. E., Anal. Chem. **33**, 1566 (1961).

CHAPTER 5

HYDROXYL COMPOUNDS

THE reactivity of hydroxyl compounds toward various reagents is dependent upon the influence of the rest of the molecule upon the hydroxyl group. On the basis of reactivity these compounds can be divided into four main classes: aliphatic alcohols, glycols, enols, and aromatic hydroxyl (phenolic) compounds.

As might be expected from the wide differences in reactivity of the various hydroxyl compounds, no single method is universally applicable to all of these compounds. The methods most generally applicable for determining macro-concentrations are based upon acylation reactions employing acetic or phthalic anhydride. Several other types of methods find considerable applicability for micro-concentrations or for obtaining greater specificity.

Methods recommended for the various classes of hydroxyl compounds are as follows:

(1) Acylation methods
   (a) Acetic anhydride methods for aliphatic alcohols, glycols, and phenols.
   (b) Phthalic anhydride method for aliphatic alcohols and glycols
(2) Periodate cleavage methods for glycols
   (a) Acid-base end determinations
   (b) Oxidation-reduction end determination
(3) Hydrogen bromide method for tertiary alcohols and certain diols
(4) Acidity methods for enols and phenols (Chapter 2)
(5) Bromination method for phenols
(6) Colorimetric methods for trace concentrations
   (a) 3,5-Dinitrobenzoyl chloride method for aliphatic alcohols and phenols

[81]

    (b) Periodate method for 1,2-glycols

    (c) Coupling methods for phenols

With the exception of the acidity methods which have been discussed previously, each of the above methods are discussed in detail as to principle, procedure, and applicability.

ACYLATION METHODS

The two acylation methods commonly used are based upon the reaction of acetic anhydride and phthalic anhydride in pyridine medium:

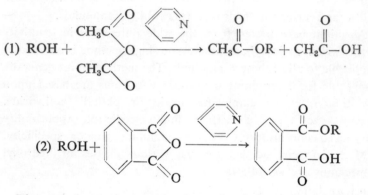

The actual reacting species in each of these cases is formed as follows:

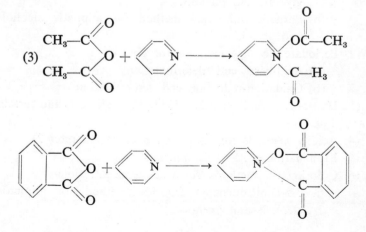

Whether the reacting species is actually a quaternary ammonium derivative or an association compound of pyridine is not definitely known. However, pyridine greatly accelerates the acylation rate over rates obtained in other solvents, indicating that the anhydride is in an activated state, probably as the quaternary derivative.

Acylation methods can be used for most primary and secondary aliphatic alcohols. Tertiary alcohols cannot be determined because these compounds tend to dehydrate to the corresponding olefin as well as acylate. However, many tertiary alcohols can be determined by reaction with hydrogen bromide [12].

The specific determination of primary or secondary alcohols cannot readily be performed with existing acylation methods because of the similarity in reactivity between the primary and secondary hydroxyl groups. However, in a few cases where the molecule contains a sterically hindered secondary hydroxyl group the reactivity with acylating reagents is retarded to such an extent that primary alcohols can be determined specifically without interference from the secondary alcohol.

Acylation with Acetic Anhydride

Acetic anhydride methods are applicable to a large number of compounds; however, these methods are subject to interference from some nonhydroxylic compounds. The phthalic anhydride method can be used in many cases where the acetic anhydride methods fail because of interferences.

Three modifications of the acetic anhydride method are particularly useful for specific cases: (1) The acetic anhydride-pyridine method; (2) The acetic anhydride-pyridine method using perchloric acid as a catalyst; and (3) The acetic anhydride-ethyl acetate method using perchloric acid as catalyst.

Acetic anhydride-pyridine method. The method most generally used in the author's laboratories is by no means original but is a modification of several methods, principally that of Wilson and Hughes [26]. The reagent concentration (12 per cent by weight acetic anhydride in pyridine) is designed to give maximum accuracy of pipeting the reagent without significantly decreasing the reactivity of the reagent by dilution.

Reagents. Acetic anhydride, 99% minimum.

Pyridine, freshly distilled, containing less than 0.02 m-equiv. per g primary and secondary amines (as determined by the carbon disulfide method in Chapter 3) and 0.1% water.

Acetic anhydride-pyridine. Add 57 ml. of acetic anhydride to 450 ml. of pyridine and shake vigorously. Add one ml. of water to stabilize the reagent. Preserve the solution in a dark-colored bottle. Discard the reagent if it becomes discolored.

Phenolphthalein indicator, 1.0% solution in pyridine.

Standard 0.5 N sodium hydroxide, carbonate-free.

Procedure. Accurately pipet 20.0 ml. of the acetic anhydride-pyridine reagent into two heat-resistant pressure bottles. Reserve one of the bottles for a blank determination. Weigh not more than 15 m-equiv. of hydroxyl compound into the other bottle. Stopper the bottles and insert them in fabric bags. Place the bottles in a steam bath at 98±2 °C for sufficient time to obtain quantitative reaction. Refer to Table 19 for the proper reaction conditions for several hydroxyl compounds. After the reaction is complete, cool the bottles to room temperature. Uncap the bottles carefully to release any pressure and remove the bags. Add clean, crushed ice until the bottles are about one-half full, then wash down the sides of the bottles with 20 to 30 ml. of distilled water. Pipet exactly 50.0 ml. of standard 0.5 N sodium hydroxide into each bottle, *agitating vigorously* during the addition. Titrate immediately with standard 0.5 N sodium hydroxide using phenolphthalein indicator.

Scope and Limitations. The acetic anhydride-pyridine method is applicable to a wide variety of hydroxyl compounds as illustrated by the examples in Table 19. The method is more accurate than most acetic anhydride methods and results for purity determinations are usually accurate to 0.2 per cent, in the absence of interferences.

Using this method, hydroxyl compounds usually require elevated temperatures for quantitative reaction, and some sterically hindered hydroxyl groups react very slowly with the reagent. For example, the secondary hydroxyl group of 2,2,4-trimethyl-1,

$$\text{3-pentanediol,} \quad \underset{\underset{\text{OH}}{|}}{\text{CH}_3}\text{—CH—CH—}\underset{\underset{\text{CH}_3}{|}}{\overset{\overset{\text{CH}_3}{|}}{\text{C}}}\text{—CH}_2\text{—OH, does not react}$$

at all at room temperature even after several hours. Both hydroxyl groups of this compound can be determined by the perchloric acid catalyzed reagent in ethyl acetate discussed subsequently.

Aromatic hydroxyl compounds react incompletely with the reagent and cannot be determined because the reagent is too dilute. These compounds can be determined by the perchloric acid catalyzed procedure.

TABLE 19

REACTION CONDITIONS FOR DETERMINING ALCOHOLS BY THE ACETIC
ANHYDRIDE-PYRIDINE METHOD

Compound	Minimum Reaction Time, min. at 98°C	Number of Reacting Groups
Allyl alcohol	30	1
Aminoethylethanolamine	15[a]	3
Butanol	30	1
Butyl Cellosolve	30	1
2-Cyclopentenol	30	1
2,4-Dichlorophenol	120	1
Diethanolamine	15	3
Diethylene glycol	30	2
Dipropylene glycol	150	2
Ethanol	30	1
Ethylene glycol	30	2
5-Ethyl-2-heptanol	240	1
2-Ethylhexanol	120	1
Glycerol	30	3
Hexanol	150	1
2-Propanol	90	1
Methanol	15	1
Propanol	30	1
Propylene glycol	120	2

[a] Room temperature.

Most primary and secondary amines react with the reagent and quantitatively interfere in hydroxyl determinations. This interference can be corrected for by an independent amine determination. The method can be used for determining primary and secondary amines; however, large quantitites of tertiary amines interfere with the end point because of the aqueous nature of the titration medium. Interference from tertiary amines can be inhibited by using a minimum amount of water to react with the excess reagent and by using a nonaqueous titrant.

Lower molecular weight aldehydes interfere in the method by an unknown mechanism. Mercaptans, tertiary alcohols, and epoxides interfere because of incomplete acetylation. Easily saponified esters such as formates also interfere.

Water will react to deplete the reagent; however, if the amount present is not excessive no interference is encountered. The following equation can be used to calculate the maximum size sample that can be used for aqueous samples:

$$\frac{0.254}{0.0094\,W + (0.01\,C + \dfrac{17.01)}{\text{equivalent weight}}} = \text{max} \cdot \text{sample size, g}$$

where W = water, per cent by weight

C = hydroxyl compound, approx. per cent by weight

This equation shows that for 20 per cent ethanol in water a maximum sample size of 0.19 g can be used, resulting in a net titration of 1.7 ml. Obviously the accuracy of such a determination is considerably limited.

Perchloric acid catalyzed acetylation in pyridine. The acetylation of hydroxyl compounds can be catalyzed by mineral acids. Fritz and Schenk [10] developed two acetylation methods using perchloric acid as the catalyst and either pyridine or ethyl acetate as the reaction medium. These authors also found that mineral acids were not effective in catalyzing phthalation reactions.

Acid catalysis in pyridine medium involves the quaternary ammonium ion formation previously discussed [10]:

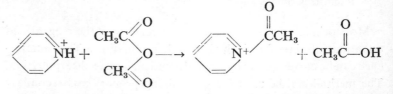

The reagent using pyridine as the solvent is less reactive than the corresponding ethyl acetate reagent, and is subject to fewer interferences. Both reagents can be used for acetylations at room temperature and therefore have this distinct advantage over other acetylating agents.

The pyridine procedure described here is a modification of the Fritz and Schenk method[10].

Reagents. Acetic anhydride, 99% minimum.

Pyridine, freshly distilled, containing less than 0.02 m-equiv./g primary and secondary amines (as determined by the carbon disulfide method in Chapter 3) and 0.1% water.

Acetylating reagent. Carefully add 4 ml. of 72 per cent perchloric acid dropwise to 240 ml. of pyridine in a 500 ml. Erlenmeyer flask. Slowly add 34 ml. of acetic anhydride. Allow the reagent to cool to room temperature. *The reagent must be prepared fresh daily.*

Phenolphthalein, 1% solution in methanol.

Standard 0.5 N potassium hydroxide in methanol.

Procedure. Accurately pipet 20.0 ml. of the acetylating reagent into two 250-ml. Erlenmeyer flasks. Reserve one of the flasks for a blank determination. Weigh not more than 10 m-equiv. of hydroxyl compound into the other flask. Allow the sample to react at room temperature for a sufficient time to obtain quantitative reaction. Refer to Table 20 for the proper reaction conditions for several hydroxyl compounds. Add 5 ml. of water to each flask and allow the flasks to stand for 5 min. Pipet exactly 50.0 ml. of standard 0.5 N methanolic potassium hydroxide into each flask. Titrate with the standard methanolic potassium hydroxide using phenolphthalein indicator.

TABLE 20

REACTION CONDITIONS FOR DETERMINING ALCOHOLS BY THE PERCHLORIC ACID CATALYZED ACETIC ANHYDRIDE-PYRIDINE METHOD

Compound	Minimum Reaction Time, min. at 25°C	Number of Reacting Groups
sec-Butanol	60	1
1-Butanol	30	1
Dipropylene glycol	60	2
Ethanol	30	1
2-Propanol	30	1
Methanol	15	1
2,4-Pentanediol	120	2
Propylene glycol	60	2

Scope and Limitations. The principal advantage of the perchloric acid catalyzed acetylating reagent is that quantitative reaction can be obtained with many alcohols at ambient temperatures. The method is also applicable to aromatic hydroxyl compounds

Because the system is essentially nonaqueous, the method can be used to determine primary and secondary amines in the presence of tertiary amines. The method is also useful for samples that have low water solubility.

The presence of perchloric acid decreases the stability of the reagent over other acetic anhydride-pyridine reagents. The reagent decreases rapidly in acetic anhydride content and must be prepared each day.

In general, the interferences encountered in this me'hod are the same as other acetic anhydride-pyridine reagents, except a greater degree of interference is encountered from carbonyl compounds. The interference from ketones can be inhibited by conducting the reaction at 0°C; however, the rate of acetylation of hydroxyl compounds is correspondingly decreased. Tertiary alcohols do not react quantitatively and usually interfere.

Perchloric acid catalyzed acetylation in ethyl acetate. The mechanism for acid catalysis in ethyl acetate medium has been postulated as follows [10]:

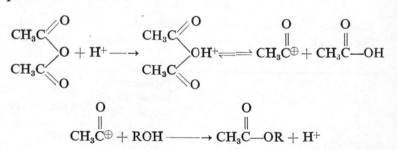

The perchloric acid catalyzed reagent in ethyl acetate is the most reactive acetylating reagent reported to date. The reagent can be used to determine most alcohols with a reaction time of less than 10 min at room temperature. The simplicity of the procedure and the rapidity with which analyses can be performed makes this method of considerable utility.

The procedure described here is a modification of the method of Fritz and Schenk [10].

Reagents. Acetic anhydride, 99% minimum.

Ethyl acetate, 99%, undenatured.

Acetylating reagent. Add 13 ml. of 72% perchloric acid to 845 ml. of ethyl acetate. Add approximately 30 ml. of acetic anhydride and allow to stand at room temperature for 30 min. Cool the reagent to 5°C and add 90 ml. of acetic anhydride previously cooled to 5°C. Allow the reagent to remain at 5°C for one hour, then allow the reagent to warm to room temperature. The reagent prepared in this manner is stable for two weeks.

Standard 0.5 N potassium hydroxide in methanol.

Phenolphthalein, 1% solution in methanol.

Procedure. Pipet exactly 20.0 ml. of the acetylating reagent into two Erlenmeyer flasks. Reserve one of the flasks for a blank determination. Weigh 10 m-equiv. of hydroxyl compound into the other flask. Allow the samples to react for a sufficient time to give quantitative reaction. Refer to Table 21 for the proper reaction conditions for several hydroxyl compounds. Add 5 ml. of water and 20 ml. of a 3·1 pyridine-water mixture. Allow the flasks to stand for 5 minutes. Accurately pipet 50.0 ml. of standard 0.5 N methanolic potassium hydroxide into each flask. Titrate with standard 0.5 N methanolic potassium hydroxide using phenolphthalein indicator.

TABLE 21

REACTION CONDITIONS FOR DETERMINING ALCOHOLS BY THE PERCHLORIC ACID CATALYZED ACETIC ANHYDRIDE-ETHYL ACETATE METHOD

Compound	Minimum Reaction Time, min. at 25°C	Number of Reacting Groups
sec-Butanol	10	1
Diisobutyl carbinol	10	1
2,2-Dimethyl-1, 3-butanediol	10	2
Heptadecanol	10	1
1,2,6-Hexanetriol	30	3
Tetradecanol	10	1
Tris(hydroxyphenyl)propane	10	3

Scope and Limitations. The perchloric acid catalyzed acetylating reagent in ethyl acetate can be used to determine many hydroxyl compounds when other acetylating reagents fail because of lack of reactivity. Both hydroxyls of 2,2,4-trimethyl-1,3-pentanediol react quantitatively by this procedure but not by other acetylating reagents. As illustrated by this example, the method can be used to determine sterically hindered secondary alcohols that react quite slowly by other acetylating reagents.

The method is applicable to aromatic hydroxyl compounds, hydroperoxides, some oximes, primary and secondary amines, and mercaptans.

The end hydroxyl groups of poly(oxyethylene) and poly(oxypropylene) compounds cannot be determined by this method because of an interfering side reaction with the polyethers.

Numerous interferences are encountered in this method because of the great reactivity of the reagent. Aldehydes, ketones, olefinic unsaturated compounds, certain ethers, imides, hydrazides, tertiary alcohols, and epoxides interfere in the method. Acetylenes and esters do not interfere.

Acylation with Phthalic Anhydride

Phthalic anhydride-pyridine methods for determining hydroxyl compounds are more selective than the acetylation methods and are therefore quite useful for circumventing interferences[6,22,]. However, the methods are applicable to fewer hydroxyl compounds.

The procedure described here is a modification of the method of Elving and Warshowsky [6].

Reagents. Phthalic anhydride, reagent grade.

Pyridine, freshly distilled, containing less than 0.02 m-equiv./g primary and secondary amines (as determined by the carbon disulfide method in Chapter 3) and 0.1% water.

Phthalic anhydride-pyridine reagent; Weigh 112 g of phthalic anhydride into 800 ml. of pyridine contained in a brown bottle. Shake the bottle vigorously until complete solution is effected. The reagent should stand for 12 hours before use, however, the solution may be heated until a slight cooling occurs.

Phenolphthalein indicator, 1% solution in pyridine.

Standard 0.5 N sodium hydroxide, carbonate-free.

Procedure. Accurately pipet 25.0 ml. of the phthalic anhydride-pyridine reagent into two heat-resistant pressure bottles. Reserve one of the bottles as a blank. Weigh 18 m-equiv. of the hydroxyl compound into the other bottle. Cap the bottles and insert each in a fabric bag. Place the bottles in a steam bath at 98°C for sufficient time to obtain quantitative reaction. Refer to Table 22 for the proper reaction conditions for several hydroxyl compounds. Cool the bottles to room temperature, remove the fabric bags, and uncap the bottles. Accurately pipet 50.0 ml. of standard 0.5 N sodium hydroxide into each bottle, swirling constantly during the addition. Titrate with standard 0.5 N sodium hydroxide using phenolphthalein indicator.

Scope and Limitations. Aldehydes and ketones do not interfere in the phthalic anhydride-pyridine method, and for this reason this method should be used, if possible, when these compounds are present.

Aromatic hydroxyl compounds cannot be determined by the method. In some cases the method can be used to determine aliphatic alcohols in the presence of phenols, provided the concentration of the latter compounds is not sufficiently great to interfere with the titrimetric end point.

The method is applicable to most aliphatic alcohols, including glycols, unless the hydroxyl groups are sterically hindered. A few of the many compounds that have been determined by the method are listed in Table 22.

The method can be applied to the determination of compounds that dehydrate quantitatively under the conditions of the acylation. In this application the excess reagent is reacted with aniline instead of water. Secondary hydroxyl compounds containing a beta

$$\text{carbonyl group such as acetaldol, } CH_3-\underset{H}{\overset{OH}{\underset{|}{C}}}-CH_2-\overset{O}{\overset{\parallel}{C}}H, \text{ dehy-}$$

drate quantitatively. This technique can also be used to estimate water.

Many primary and secondary amines react quantitatively with the reagent but in some cases over-acylation is obtained. For this reason, acetic anhydride methods should be used for samples that contain amines. Aliphatic tertiary amines are sufficiently basic to interfere with the indicator end point under the essentially aqueous conditions of the titration. This type of interference can be inhibited by reacting the excess reagent with a minimum amount of water, and by employing a nonaqueous titrant.

Mercaptans, epoxides, and easily saponified esters, such as formates interfere in the method.

TABLE 22

REACTION CONDITIONS FOR DETERMINING ALCOHOLS BY THE PHTHALIC ANHYDRIDE-PYRIDINE METHOD

Compound	Minimum Reaction Time, min. at 98°C	Number of Reacting Groups
Butanol	30	1
2-Cyclopentenol	30	1
Diethylene glycol	15	2
2,6-Dimethyl-4-pentanol	120	1
Dipropylene glycol	150	2
Ethanol	30	1
2-Ethylbutanol	30	1
2-Ethyl-1,3-hexanediol	180	2
2-Heptanol	120	1
2-Propanol	90	1
Methanol	15	1
Pentaerythritol	15	4
1,5-Pentanediol	30	2
Propanol	30	1

CLEAVAGE OF 1,2-GLYCOLS

1,2-Glycols can be determined by the acylation methods previously discussed. However, a greater degree of specificity is obtained by utilizing the methods based upon cleavage by periodate as follows [17]:

$$\overset{\displaystyle OH \quad\; OH}{\underset{\displaystyle |\quad\;\; |}{R-CH-CH-R'}} + IO_4^- \longrightarrow RCH=O + R'CH=O + IO_3^- + H_2O$$

In the case of ethylene glycol, two moles of formaldehyde are formed. A mole of formaldehyde and a mole of acetaldehyde are formed from propylene glycol, $HCH\!-\!CH\!-\!CH_3$. The internal

$$\underset{OH\quad OH}{\mid\qquad\mid}$$

hydroxyl group of glycerol is oxidized to formic acid, while the terminal groups are oxidized to formaldehyde.

Certain glycols can also be determined by reaction with hydrogen bromide. This procedure will be discussed subsequently in the section devoted to tertiary alcohols.

Three general periodate methods are of value for determining 1,2-glycols: (1) The acid-base method using sodium metaperiodate $(NaIO_4)$; (2) The oxidation-reduction method using periodic acid; and (3) The colorimetric measurement of the formaldehyde reaction product. The latter method will be discussed in the section on colorimetric methods.

Sodium Metaperiodate Method

The end determination of the sodium metaperiodate method[3,4,18] is based on the fact that in water the following equilibrium is established with the reagent:

$$NaIO_4 + 2H_2O \rightleftharpoons NaH_4IO_6$$

The sodium paraperiodate formed by hydration of the reagent is acidic and can be titrated with sodium hydroxide, consuming one mole of base. Sodium iodate formed as a product of the cleavage of a glycol is neutral to the indicator used. Hence, a decrease in acidity is a measure of 1,2-glycol cleaved by the reagent.

Good accuracy is obtained in the modification described here by conducting the titration at reduced temperature, thus increasing the sharpness of the end point[4].

Reagents. Sodium metaperiodate $(NaIO_4)$, 0.1 M.
Standard 0.1 N sodium hydroxide, carbonate-free.
Mixed indicator, 0.4% thymolphthalein and 0.2% 1-naphtholbenzein in 90% v/v ethanol-water.

Procedure. Accurately pipet 50.0 ml. of the sodium metaperiodate reagent into two Erlenmeyer flasks. Reserve one of the flasks as a blank. Weigh (or use an aliquot of a dilution) 3.5 m-equiv. of 1,2-glycol into the other flask. Allow the flasks to stand for a sufficient time to give quantitative reaction. Most 1,2-glycols will react quantitatively in 20 min. Add enough crushed ice to each flask to reduce the temperature of the solution to 1°C and to maintain this temperature during the titration. Add 2 ml. of the mixed indicator to each flask and titrate with standard 0.1 N sodium hydroxide to a grayish-blue color. Match the color of the sample to that of the blank.

Scope and Limitations. The sodium periodate method is applicable to most 1,2-glycols, and a reaction time of 20 min at room temperature is usually sufficient for quantitative results. The standard deviation for determining the purity of ethylene glycol for 13° freedom is 0.24.

Compounds that contain a secondary hydroxyl group that can be oxidized to formic acid, such as glycerol, can be determined specifically by a modification of this method. In this application the formic acid formed is titrated, using methyl red as the indicator, after reduction of the excess periodate ion with ethylene glycol.

Because the end determination is based upon an acid-base titration, acidic or basic compounds interfere. Acids with ionization constants greater than 1×10^{-6} interfere quantitatively and can be corrected for. Weak bases, such as amines, cannot be tolerated; however, bases with ionization constants greater than 1×10^{-2} can be present in concentrations up to 0.5 milliequivalent if corrections are made.

Certain vicinal compounds other than 1,2-glycols will undergo cleavage reactions and interfere. Compounds that interfere in this respect contain the following groups:

$$\underset{\underset{\textstyle -C-C-}{\overset{\textstyle \| \quad \|}{}}}{\overset{\textstyle O \quad O}{}};\quad \underset{\underset{\textstyle -C-C-}{\overset{\textstyle \| \quad |}{}}}{\overset{\textstyle O \quad OH}{}};\quad \text{and}\quad \underset{\underset{\textstyle -C-C-}{\overset{\textstyle | \quad |}{}}}{\overset{\textstyle H_2N \quad OH}{}}.$$

Compounds of the former two types can sometimes be determined quantitatively.

Periodic Acid (Redox) Method

Oxidation-reduction end determinations for 1,2-glycols are not affected by the acid-base characteristics of the sample as is the previous method. For this reason this modification is preferred for samples that contain amines or other basic or acidic components.

In the modification described here (14, 20) unreacted periodic acid is reacted with an excess of sodium arsenite, and the excess sodium arsenite is titrated with standard iodine.

Reagents. Periodic acid, 0.1 M. Dissolve 22.8 g reagent grade periodic acid ($HIO_4 \cdot 2H_2O$) in 400 ml. of 0.5 N sulfuric acid. Dilute to one liter with water.

Sodium arsenite, 0.1 N. Dissolve 4,0 g of sodium hydroxide pellets and 5.0 g of arsenous oxide in a minimum amount of water. Add 10.0 g of sodium bicarbonate and dilute to one liter with water.

Iodine, 0.1 N.

Starch indicator, 1%.

Potassium iodide, 15%.

Sodium bicarbonate, reagent grade.

Sodium bicarbonate, saturated solution.

Procedure. Transfer 50 ml. of distilled water to two Erlenmeyer flasks. Reserve one of the flasks as a blank. Weigh not more than 2.0 m-equiv. (use a dilution for pure compounds) of 1,2-glycol into the other flask and swirl to dissolve the sample. Accurately pipet 15.0 ml. of the periodic acid reagent into each flask. Allow the flasks to stand for 20 min at room temperature. Add 30 ml. of saturated sodium bicarbonate solution to each flask. Accurately pipet 50.0 ml. of 0.1 N sodium arsenite into each flask and allow the flasks to stand for 10 min. Add one ml. of the 15 per cent potassium iodide solution, 2 ml. of the starch solution, and 10 to 12 g of sodium bicarbonate. Titrate with standard 0.1 N iodine to the appearance of the first blue color. If the difference between the sample and the blank exceeds 20 ml., repeat the analysis using a smaller sample size.

Scope and Limitations. This periodate method can be used to determine most 1,2-glycols and 1,2-amino alcohols. Ethanolamine, $NH_2CH_2CH_2OH$, and diethanolamine, $HN(CH_2CH_2OH)_2$, react quantitatively but the corresponding tertiary amine does not react at all.

Amines do not interfere in this procedure, as in other procedures, because the amino nitrogen in the form of the sulfate is more resistant to oxidation by periodate ion, than is the free amine or the amine acetate.

The method is not as accurate as the acid-base method (overoxidation tends to occur) but is subject to fewer interferences.

HYDROGEN BROMIDE METHOD FOR TERTIARY ALCOHOLS (AND DIOLS)

Because of their tendency to dehydrate, tertiary alcohols cannot be determined by most acylation methods. The only satisfactory functional group method for this class of alcohols is based upon their quantitative reaction with hydrogen bromide in glacial acetic acid [12]:

$$R_3COH + HBr \longrightarrow R_3CBr + HOH$$

The unreacted hydrogen bromide is titrated with sodium acetate in acetic acid using crystal violet as the indicator.

Reagents. Glacial acetic acid, Grasselli grade.

Hydrogen bromide, approximately 0.5 N. Carefully add 67 ml. of reagent grade bromine to 2 l. of glacial acetic acid. Add reagent grade phenol in 10 g increments until the solution becomes light straw in color (approximately 100 g) and add 10 g in excess. Allow the solution to stand at least 12 hr.

Standard 0.2 N sodium acetate in acetic acid. Standardize against standard 0.2 N perchloric acid in acetic acid which has been previously standardized against potassium acid phthalate.

Crystal violet indicator, 1.0% solution in acetic acid.

Procedure. Accurately pipet 25.0 ml. of the hydrogen bromide reagent into two 250-ml. iodine flasks. Reserve one of the flasks as a blank. Weigh not more than 6 m-equiv. of tertiary alcohol into the other flask. Stopper the flasks, using 5 ml. of acetic acid as a liquid seal, and allow the samples to stand for a sufficient time to give quantitative reaction (usually 1 hr). Wash down the inside walls of the flasks with 25 ml. of acetic acid. Add 5 or 6 drops of the crystal violet indicator and titrate with the standard 0.2 N sodium acetate to the appearance of a blue-green color.

Scope and Limitations. The hydrogen bromide method for tertiary alcohols is also applicable to 1,2- and certain 1,3-glycols. Some of the compounds that have been determined by this method are listed in Table 23.

Strong mineral acids and most bases interfere, but can be corrected for. Most epoxides also interfere quantitatively in the method. Conjugated-dienes, conjugated carbonyl compounds, isobutylene, cyclopropane derivatives, and peroxides react with the reagent and consequently interfere.

Large quantities of water or alcohols will interfere because they tend to be basic to the indicator, as well as retard the rate of reaction with tertiary alcohols. The water concentration in the final titration medium should be below 0.3 per cent. For this reason the reagent must be prepared by the reaction of bromine with phenol, instead of from concentrated aqueous acid commercially available.

TABLE 23

REACTION CONDITIONS FOR THE DETERMINATION OF TERTIARY ALCOHOLS AND CERTAIN DIOLS BY REACTION WITH HYDROGEN BROMIDE

Compound	Minimum Reaction Time, hours at 25°C
tert-Butanol	1
2,7-Dimethyl-2,7-octanediol	1[a]
Ethylene glycol	4
Propylene glycol	4
2-Ethyl-1,3-hexanediol	2

[a] Two reacting groups.

BROMINATION METHOD FOR AROMATIC HYDROXYL COMPOUNDS

Aromatic hydroxyl compounds will react with bromine, via a substitution reaction, at the positions *ortho* and *para* to the hydroxyl group:

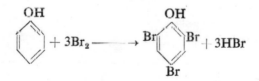

and

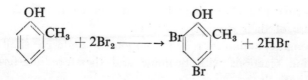

This principle has been used extensively as the basis of procedures for determining aromatic hydroxyl compounds [16,23,13]. The procedure described here is essentially that of Ingberman[13].

Reagents. Glacial acetic acid, Graselli grade.
Pyridine, 27 v/v % in acetic acid.
Bromine reagent, 0.3 N in acetic acid.
Sodium thiosulfate, 0.15 N.
Potassium iodide, 50%.
Starch indicator, 1%.

Procedure. Pressure pipet exactly 25.0 ml. of the bromine reagent into two iodine flasks. Reserve one of the flasks as a blank. Weigh not more than 4.5 m-equiv. of aromatic hydroxyl compound into the other flask. Add 1 ml. of the pyridine solution and allow the flasks to stand for 2 to 20 min at room temperature. Add 75 ml. of water and 5 ml. of potassium iodide to each flask. Titrate with the standard sodium thiosulfate using starch indicator.

Scope and Limitations. This method is applicable to many aromatic hydroxyl compounds that have unsubstituted ortho and/or para positions (see Table 24). Most mono-alkyl substituted phenols react quantitatively and can be determined.

TABLE 24

BROMINATION OF AROMATIC HYDROXYL COMPOUNDS

Compound	Number of Reacting Positions
p-tert-Butylphenol	2
2,6-Bis (o-hydroxybenzyl) phenol	5
m-Cresol	3
p-Cresol	2
2,2′-Dihydroxydiphenylmethane	4
2,4′-Dihydroxydiphenylmethane	4
p-Hydroxybenzyl alcohol	2
Phenol	3

Di-*tert.*-alkylphenols tend to over-brominate presumably by replacement of the alkyl group. Other groups substituted on the ring, such as formyl and carboxyl, may also cause high results. Dihydroxy phenols such as hydroquinone cannot be determined because of their ease of oxidation.

Aromatic amino nitrogen compounds undergo similar substitution reactions with bromine and therefore interfere, some quantitatively.

Most aldehydes and olefins interfere; the former compounds by oxidation and the latter by addition of bromine.

COLORIMETRIC METHODS

The determination of trace concentrations of hydroxyl compounds cannot ordinarily be performed by the titrimetric methods previously discussed, because of their inherent lack of sensitivity. For this reason, colorimetric methods are generally employed for determinations in the ppm range.

Methods that have been used for aliphatic alcohols are the cerate method[21], the dichromate oxidation method[1,2], and the 3,5-dinitrobenzoyl chloride method[15]. 1,2-Glyocols have been determined by cleaving to formaldehyde and determining the latter compound colorimetrically[24]. Aromatic hydroxyl compounds undergo numerous color reactions, and therefore many different colorimetric methods have been described. Because of their wide differences in reactivity, phenolic compounds and aliphatic alcohols cannot usually be determined by the same methods.

Aliphatic Alcohols

The cerate method for alcohols is based upon the formation of a colored complex by reaction of the alcohol with ammonium hexanitrato cerate[5]. The dichromate oxidation method of Aguhlon is based upon the selective oxidation of the alcohol, and the corresponding reduction of dichromate ion to the blue chromic ion[1,2]. The amount of blue color formed is a measure of the alcohol oxidized.

Because both of these methods employ oxidizing reagents in acidic media, other easily oxidized compounds and compounds that acid hydrolyze to alcohols or easily oxidized compounds will interfere. Among a few of the interferences encountered are aldehydes, vinyl ethers, acetals, ketals, and certain esters.

3,5-Dinitrobenzoyl chloride method. In pyridine medium 3, 5-dinitrobenzoyl chloride reacts quantitatively with most primary and secondary alcohols to form the corresponding dinitrobenzoate esters:

7*

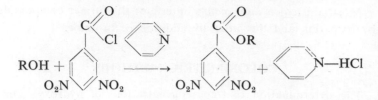

The solution is made aqueous by the addition of sufficient hydrochloric acid to neutralize the pyridine, and the esters are separated by extraction into hexane.

The separated benzoate esters are reacted with sodium hydroxide to form a blue color. Presumably, the color reaction is the formation of a resonating quinoidal ion structure.

Reagents. 3,5-Dinitrobenzoyl chloride, 10 wt/vol % in pyridine. Heat to effect solution if necessary, and prepare the reagent just before using.

Pyridine, redistilled.

n-Hexane.

Acetone, reagent grade.

Hydrochloric acid, 2N.

Sodium hydroxide, 5%.

Procedure. Prepare a 100 ml. dilution of the sample in pyridine containing no more than 0.3 m-moles of hydroxyl compound. Transfer 2.0 ml. of the dilution to a 100-ml. glass-stoppered graduated cylinder. Add 1 ml. of the 3,5-dinitrobenzoyl chloride solution and react for 10 min. Add 25 ml. of 2N hydrochloric acid and mix. Pipet 20 ml. of hexane into the cylinder, stopper and shake vigorously. Allow the phases to separate and pipet 2 ml. of the hexane layer into a 25-ml. glass-stoppered graduated cylinder. Pipet 10 ml. of acetone and 0.3 ml. of 2N sodium hydroxide into the cylinder. Stopper and shake well for 10 sec. Immediately determine the absorbance at a wavelength of 575 mμ, using 1 cm cells, against a blank prepared in an identical manner. The color is only stable for 5 min. Determine the concentration of alcohol from a calibration curve prepared with any high-purity primary or secondary monofunctional alcohol.

Scope and Limitations. Because the reaction with 3,5-dinitrobenzoyl chloride takes place in basic media, this method is ideally suited for determining low concentrations of alcohols in the presence of acid hydrolyzable compounds such as acetals, ketals, vinyl ethers, and esters. The method is also applicable in the presence of easily oxidized compounds.

Most primary and secondary monohydroxy alcohols react quantitatively with the reagent to form water insoluble esters that can be extracted and therefore determined. 1,2-Glycols and other dihydroxy-compounds react quantitatively, but cannot be extracted from the aqueous solution, and therefore cannot be determined. Some compounds that can be determined by the method are listed in Table 25.

TABLE 25

DETERMINATION OF ALCOHOLS BY THE 3,5-DINITROBENZOYL CHLORIDE METHOD

Compound	Lower Limit of Determination, ppm[a]
Methanol	2.8
Ethanol	4.1
2-Propanol	5.3
Butanol	6.5
Hexanol	9.0
5-Ethyl-2-heptanol	12.7
Eicosanol (C-20)	14.9

[a] Based on a 1 g nonaqueous sample and an absorbance of 0.01.

Because the color reaction is based upon the quinoidal ion formation of the aromatic ring and is independent of the alcohol, all alcohols give colors proportional to their molecular weight. Therefore, a separate calibration curve is not necessary for each alcohol determined.

Interferences in the method are generally restricted to compounds that react to deplete the reagent. Water interferes in this respect. Primary and secondary amines react but the amides formed are not extractable in hexane. The interference from compounds that deplete the reagent can be obviated somewhat by increasing the reagent concentration. Although water quantitatively consumes the reagent, as little as 0.6 per cent ethanol can be determined in water by this technique. When lower concentrations of alcohols are to be determined in water, either the Aguhlon[1,2] or the cerate[21] methods should be used, provided that other interferences are not encountered.

Colorimetric method for 1,2-glycols. The determination of trace concentrations of 1,2-glycols can be quite satisfactorily performed by cleaving with periodate ion, and determining the formaldehyde formed by its color reaction with chromotropic acid[24]. The method can be used for determining as little as 1 ppm 1,2-glycols in 10 g of a water soluble sample.

The modification described here is essentially that of Speck and Forist[24].

Reagents. Sodium periodate, 0.1 M.

Sodium sulfite, 5.5% solution. Prepare fresh reagent at least once every week.

Sodium chromotropate (sodium 1,8-dihydroxynaphthalene-3,5-disulfonate).

Sulfuric acid, 95%.

Procedure. Add 2.0 ml of 0.1 N sodium periodate to two 100-ml. glass-stoppered graduated cylinders. Reserve one of the cylinders as a blank. Transfer an amount of 1,2-glycol to the other cylinder, not exceeding the equivalent of 0.7 mg of formaldehyde. Dilute to 20 ml. with water and react for one hour at room temperature. Pipet 2.0 ml. of the sodium sulfite into each cylinder and dilute to 100 ml. with water, stopper, and mix.

Transfer 10 ml. aliquots of each dilution to 100-ml. glass-stoppered graduated cylinders. Add 0.05±0.01 g of sodium chromotropate to each cylinder and dissolve. Dilute to 50 ml. with concentrated sulfuric acid and allow the normal heat rise to occur. By means of a 20-ml. pipet or capillary glass tubing connected to a nitrogen source and immersed in the acid solution, ebullate vigorously with nitrogen for approximately 10 min. When the contents have cooled to room temperature, measure the absorbance of the sample versus the blank at 570 mµ using 1 cm cells. Read the concentration of 1,2-glycol from a calibration curve prepared from the glycol being determined.

Scope and Limitations. This colorimetric method is applicable to most 1,2-glycols and is ideally suited for trace determinations. Since the end determination is based upon a color reaction of formaldehyde, formaldehyde must be a product of the periodate cleavage. 1,2-Glycols of the following type cannot be determined; R–CH–CH–R, where R is alkyl.
$$\begin{array}{cc} | & | \\ OH & OH \end{array}$$

Formaldehyde and other vicinal compounds that cleave with periodate to form formaldehyde will interfere in this method. Interferences are sometimes also encountered from large concentrations of organic compounds that will discolor in hot, concentrated sulfuric acid. Aldehydes are particularly bad in this respect.

Aromatic Hydroxyl Compounds

The large number of color reactions that are available for aromatic hydroxyl compounds are usually based upon a coupling reaction in the ortho or para position:

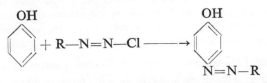

Methods of this type are the Gibbs method using 2,6-dibromoquinone chlorimide[8,11]

$O=\langle\rangle=N-Cl$, methods using diazotized sulphanilic acid[19]

or *p*-nitroaniline[25], and the 4-aminoantipyrine method[7,9]. The latter method is very sensitive and has been studied in detail.

4-Aminoantipyrine method. Phenolic compounds react with 4-aminoantipyrine in the presence of alkaline oxidizing agents to form antipyrine dyes:

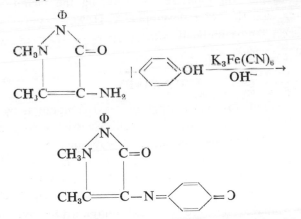

These dyes can be extracted from aqueous solution with chloroform and absorb at a wavelength of 460 mμ.

Reagents. 4-Aminoantipyrine, 3%.
Potassium ferricyanide, 2%.
Ammonium hydroxide, 6N.

Procedure. Adjust the pH of an aqueous dilution of the sample, containing no more than 50 μg of phenolic compound, to 9.8 to 10.2 with 6N ammonium hydroxide. Dilute to 500 ml. with distilled water. Add 1.0 ml. of the aminoantipyrine reagent. Add 10 ml. of the potassium ferricyanide reagent. Transfer the solution to a separatory funnel and extract with 15, 10, and 5 ml. volumes of chloroform. Combine the chloroform extracts and adjust the volume to 30 ml. Filter the solution and measure the absorbance against a blank in 1-cm cells at a wavelength of 460 mμ. The color is stable for 10 min.

Scope and Limitations. Using a 500-ml. sample this method can be used to determine as little as 0.01 ppm aromatic hydroxyl compounds with an accuracy of 5 per cent.

The method is applicable to most phenolic compounds substituted in the ortho and meta position. Phenolic compounds substituted in the para position by hydroxyl, or methoxy groups can also be determined.

The method is not applicable to phenolic compounds substituted in the para position by aryl, alkyl, nitro, nitroso, benzoyl, or aldehyde groups.

Aromatic amines unsubstituted in the para position will undergo the color reaction and interfere. Certain inorganic oxidizing or reducing agents will interfere by oxidizing the phenol or by interfering with the color development. However, most of these interferences can be inhibited by prior separation from the hydroxyl compound.

SUMMARY

Three methods for determining hydroxyl compounds by acetylation with acetic anhydride have been discussed in this chapter. The acetic anhydride-pyridine method is reasonably accurate and is applicable to a variety of alcohols. The method is not recommended for sterically hindered alcohols or aromatic hydroxyl compounds. The perchloric acid-catalyzed acetylation methods are valuable because elevated temperatures are not required for quantitative reaction. The catalyzed reagent in ethyl acetate is applicable to most hydroxyl compounds, but is subject to interferences from several non-hydroxylic compounds. The corresponding reagent in pyridine is less subject to such interferences, but is less reactive.

The phthalic anhydride-pyridine method is particularly valuable for determining hydroxyl compounds, in the presence of aldehydes which tend to interfere in the acetylation methods.

The macro determination of 1,2-glycols can be performed readily using either the sodium metaperiodate (acid-base) method or the periodic acid (redox) method. These procedures complement each other in that they are subject to different types of interferences. Trace concentrations of certain 1,2-glycols are more readily determined by a colorimetric periodate method that is based upon the cleavage to formaldehyde and the subsequent determination of the latter compound.

Tertiary alcohols can be determined by reaction with hydrogen bromide in glacial acetic acid to form the corresponding bromide. This is one of the few methods available for such determinations.

Although aromatic hydroxyl compounds can be determined by acetylation methods, a method based upon bromination of the aromatic ring is of value, particularly for analyzing mixtures of aliphatic and aromatic hydroxyl compounds.

Low concentrations of alcohols can be determined by a colorimetric method based upon the reaction with 3,5-dinitrobenzoyl chloride to form the corresponding benzoate esters. These esters are extracted, and colored derivatives are formed by treatment with a base. The method is capable of considerably better sensitivity than volumetric procedures. Aromatic hydroxyl compounds can be determined more readily by a colorimetric method based upon reaction with 4-aminoantipyrine.

REFERENCES

1. AGULHON, H., *Bull. Soc. Chim.*, **9**, 881 (1911).
2. AGULHON, H., *Ann. Chim. Anal.*, **17**, 50 (1912).
3. BRADFORD, P., POHLE. W. D., GUNTHER, J. K., MEHLENBACHER, V. C., *Oil and Soap*, **19**, 189 (1942).
4. DAL NOGARE, S., OEMLER, A. N., *Anal. Chem.*, **24**, 902 (1952).
5. DUKE, F. R., SMITH, G. F., *Ind. Eng. Chem., Anal. Ed.*, **12**, 201 (1940),

6. ELVING, P. J., WARSHOWSKY, B., *Anal. Chem.*, **19**, 1006 (1947).
7. EMERSON, E., *J. Org. Chem.*, **8**, 417 (1943).
8. ETTINGER, M. B., RUCHHOFT, C. C., *Anal. Chem.*, **20**, 1191 (1948).
9. ETTINGER, M. B., RUCHHOFT, C. C., LISKA, R. J., *Anal. Chem.*, **23**, 1783 (1951).
10. FRITZ, J. S., SCHENK, G. H.,*Anal. Chem.*, **31**, 1808 (1959).
11. GIBBS, H. D., *J. Biol. Chem.*, **72**, 649 (1927).
12. HOGSETT, J. N., unpublished data, Union Carbide Chemicals Company, South Charleston, W. Va.
13. INGBERMAN, A. K., *Anal. Chem.*, **30**, 1003 (1958).
14. JACKSON, E. L., *Organic Reactions* Vol. II, pp. 341, John Wiley., New York, 1944.
15. JOHNSON, D. P., CRITCHFIELD, F. E., *Anal. Chem.*, **32**, 865 (1960).
16. KOPPESCHAAR, W. F., *Z. Anal. Chem.*, **15**, 233 (1876).
17. MALAPRADE, M. L., *Bull. soc. chim. France* (4), **43**, 683 (1928).
18. MALAPRADE, M. L., *Bull. soc. chim.* (5) **4**, 906 (1937).
19. MILLER, J. N., URBAIN, M., *Ind. Eng. Chem. Anal. Ed.*, **2**, 123 (1930).
20. NICOLET, B. H., SHINN, L. A., *J. Amer. Chem. Soc.*, **61**, 1615 (1939).
21. REID, V. W., TRUCLOVE, R. K., *Analyst*, **77**, 325 (1952).
22. SABETAY, S., NAVES, Y. R., *Am. Chim. Anal. Chim. Appl.*, **19**, 35 (1937).
23. SCOTT, R. D., *Ind. Eng. Chem. Anal. Ed.*, **3**, 67 (1931).
24. SPECK, J. C., Jr. and FORIST, A. A., *Anal. Chem.*, **26**, 1942 (1954).
25. THEIS, R. C., BENEDICT, S. R., *J. Biol. Chem.*, **61**, 67 (1924).
26. WILSON, H. N., HUGHES, W. C., *J. Soc. Chem. Ind.*, **58**, 74 (1939).

CHAPTER 6

UNSATURATED COMPOUNDS

NUMEROUS methods have been developed for determining carbon to carbon unsaturation because this type of functional group undergoes a wide variety of reactions, many of which can be quantitative. The extent to which these reactions take place depends upon the nature of the unsaturation.

The behavior of olefinic unsaturated compounds is markedly different from that of acetylinic unsaturated compounds; therefore, different types of reagents are used for these classes of compounds. Olefinic unsaturated compounds can be classified according to reactivity, and some of the more important classes are as follows:

(1) Isolated unsaturation: R–CH=CH–R

(2) Conjugated dienes: R–CH=CH–CH=CH–R

(3) α, β-Unsaturation: R–CH=CH–X, where X is any electron-withdrawing group

(4) Vinyl unsaturation: CH_2=CH–R

No single method can be used to determine all compounds of these classes; therefore, several methods are presented in this chapter and each has its advantages and disadvantages.

Halogenation methods are commonly used for determining olefinic unsaturation; however, these methods are not ideally suited for all cases, particularly, α, β-unsaturated compounds and vinyl ethers. The halogenation methods included in this chapter are the bromine-bromide (Kaufmann) method, the pyridinium sulfate dibromide method, and the Wijs method.

Other types of methods that have unique advantages are the morpholine method for α, β-unsaturated compounds, the mercuric acetate method, and the silver perchlorate method for acetylinic compounds. These too, are described in this chapter.

[107]

HALOGENATION METHODS

Halogenation methods are applicable to a wide variety of types of olefinic unsaturation; however, these methods do have their limitations, particularly, with respect to reactivity toward certain types of unsaturation and interferences. In the following discussion, three halogenation methods are presented. These particular methods were selected from the large reservoir of halogenation methods because of their general utility.

Bromine-Bromide Method for Olefinic Unsaturation

One of the major limitations of most halogenation methods is the occurrence of substitution reactions instead of the desired addition reaction. The substitution of bromine for hydrogen is catalyzed by ultraviolet light, and occurs most readily with a hydrogen atom bonded to a tertiary carbon atom.

Substitution reactions that normally occur with halogenation reagents can be considerably minimized by using a reagent of bromine in methanol containing saturated sodium bromide[6]. Under these conditions, the tribromide ion, Br_3^-, formed does not readily undergo substitution reactions, but is still a good brominating agent. The reagent also possesses the further advantage of being relatively stable, since the volatility of bromine is decreased by formation of the tribromide ion.

The procedure described here is a modification of the original method of Kaufmann[6].

Reagents. Bromine-bromide reagent, 0.2 N. Add 5.5 ml. of reagent-grade bromine to a volumetric flask containing 500 ml. of methanol and 100 g of reagent-grade sodium bromide. Mix and dilute to volume with methanol. Transfer to a quart bottle and fit the bottle with a two-hole rubber stopper. Insert a 25-ml. pipet into one of the holes so that the tip extends below the surface of the liquid. Insert a piece of glass tubing through the other hole and attach an aspirator bulb to the tubing. Use pressure pipeting for all subsequent transfers of reagent.
Sodium bromide, reagent grade.
Sodium bromide, saturated aqueous solution.
Potassium iodide, 15% aqueous solution.
Sodium thiosulfate, standard 0.1 N solution.

Procedure. Add 10 ml. of saturated sodium bromide and approximately one g of sodium bromide to each of two glass-stoppered Erlenmeyer flasks. Pressure pipet 25.0 ml. of the bromine-bromide reagent into each flask. Reserve one of the flasks for a blank determination. If the reaction is to be conducted at —10°C, cool the flasks to this temperature. Weigh no more than 4.0 m-equiv. of unsaturated compound into one of the flasks. Allow the flasks to stand for sufficient time and at the optimum temperature for quantitative results. Consult Table 26 for the reaction conditions for a few unsaturated compounds. Add 75 ml. of methanol and 10 ml. of 15% potassium iodide to each flask and immediately titrate with the standard sodium thiosulfate to the disappearance of the yellow color.

Scope and Limitations. The bromine-bromide method has been applied to a wide variety of unsaturated compounds, a few of which are listed in Table 26. The method is applicable to most compounds containing isolated and vinyl type unsaturation. Using the method as presented, excessive reaction times are obtained for most vinyl ethers; however, this can be obviated by doubling all of the reagent volumes used in the method.

TABLE 26

REACTION CONDITIONS FOR UNSATURATED COMPOUNDS
BY THE BROMINE-BROMIDE METHOD

Compound	Reaction Conditions	
	Temp., °C	Time, min.
Allyl alcohol	25	90
Crotonaldehyde	—10	30
Crotonic acid	25	210
Cyclohexene	25	45
2-Ethylcrotonaldehyde	—10	60
Furfural	—10	45
1-Heptene	25	60
Isoprene	25	60
Mesityl oxide	25	60
2-Methyl-2-pentenal	—10	45
2-Methyl-5-vinylpyridine	25	5
Styrene	25	45
Vinyl acetate	25	5
Vinyl 2-chloroethyl ether	—10	30
Vinyl formate	25	5

The method is not applicable to α, β-unsaturated compounds containing the following electron-withdrawing groups: $-COOH$, $-COOR$, $CONH_2$, $-SO_3H$, $C\equiv N$. These compounds brominate very slowly.

The method is applicable to α, β-unsaturated aldehydes provided the reaction is conducted at $-10°C$ to inhibit oxidation of the aldehyde. When the method is used to determine unsaturation in the presence of saturated aldehydes, reduced temperature should also be used to inhibit oxidative interference.

There is some evidence that certain compounds containing tertiary carbon atoms will undergo substitution reactions with this reagent; however, substitution is normally not a problem with the reagent. Interference can be encountered from the oxidation of secondary alcohols, but this can be minimized by using reduced temperatures for the reaction.

The method is not directly applicable to the determination of unsaturation in the presence of primary and secondary amines, but the incorporation of sufficient acetic acid into the reagent to neutralize the amines will inhibit their oxidation. Oxidation will also occur with peroxides and other easily oxidized materials.

Bromine-Bromide Method for α, β-Unsaturated Compounds

As previously mentioned, compounds that have an unsaturation conjugated to a strong electron-withdrawing group are difficult to brominate. Compounds included in this class are acrylic, methacrylic, maleic, and fumaric acids and esters. However, these compounds can be determined by the bromine-bromide method provided they are converted to the sodium or potassium salts prior to bromination[4]. The addition of bromine to the unsaturation of the salts is rapid and complete, because neutralization of the carboxyl group decreases the electron-withdrawing tendency of this group.

In the method described here, α, β-unsaturated acids are neutralized with sodium hydroxide and then brominated, while α, β-unsaturated esters are saponified to convert them to the alkali metal salts. Excess alkali metal hydroxide is neutralized before the bromination because it will irreversibly consume bromine.

Reagents. With the exception of the following, the same reagents are used as in the previous bromine-bromide method:

Potassium hydroxide, 1.0 N.

Sodium hydroxide, 0.5 N.

Hydrochloric acid, 0.5 N.

Phenolphthalein indicator, 1.0 % solution in methanol.

Procedure: α, β-*Unsaturated Esters.* Transfer 25 ml. of 1.0 N potassium hydroxide into each of two 100-ml. volumetric flasks. Reserve one flask as a blank. Weigh 35 m-equiv. based on 1 N potassium hydroxide, (or 23 m-equiv. for maleic or fumaric esters) of unsaturated compound into the other flasks. Add 10 ml. of acetone as co-solvent if required for the high molecular weight esters (see Table 27). Stopper the flasks and place them on a mechanical shaker until the saponification is complete (see Table 27). Remove the flasks from the shaker and carefully neutralize the excess potassium hydroxide using 0.5 N hydrochloric acid and phenolphthalein indicator. If necessary, add a very slight excess of 0.5 N sodium hydroxide so that the solution is a faint pink. Dilute to 100 ml. with water and mix. Continue with the bromination procedure described below.

α, β-*Unsaturated Acids.* Add 15 to 20 ml. of distilled water to two 100-ml. volumetric flasks. Reserve one of the flasks as a blank. Weigh not more than 17.5 m-equiv. (based on 0.5 N sodium hydroxide) of unsaturated compound into one of the flasks. Neutralize the sample to phenolphthalein indicator using 0.5 N sodium hydroxide. Dilute to 100 ml. with water and mix. Continue with the bromination procedure.

Bromination. Pipet 10.0 ml. (or 15.0 ml. for maleic and fumaric esters) aliquots of the sample and blank dilutions to respective 250-ml. glass-stoppered Erlenmeyer flasks. Add sufficient distilled water to make a total of 20 ml. Add 10 ml. of saturated sodium bromide and 4 to 6 g of the solid sodium bromide to each flask (omit the solid sodium bromide when analyzing fumaric compounds). Pipet 25.0 ml. of the bromine-bromide reagent into each flask and allow the flasks to stand until the bromination is complete (see Table 27). Add 75 ml. of methanol, 10 ml. of 15% potassium iodide, and 2 ml. of glacial acetic acid to each flask. Titrate immediately with standard 0.1 N thiosulfate to the disappearance of the yellow color.

Scope and Limitations. This method can be applied to most α, β-unsaturated acids and esters. The reaction conditions for several of these compounds are shown in Table 27. The limiting factor in applying the method to α, β-unsaturated esters is the saponification procedure. High molecular weight esters are insoluble in the saponification medium and are, therefore, difficult to saponify. Alcohols are commonly used as co-solvents for saponification reactions, but cannot be used in this case because of the following side reaction:

$$CH_2{=}CH\overset{\overset{\Large O}{\|}}{C}OR + ROH \xrightleftharpoons{OH^-} ROCH_2CH_2\overset{\overset{\Large O}{\|}}{C}OR$$

Acetone can be used as a co-solvent, but the amount that is miscible with the potassium hydroxide reagent is limited.

TABLE 27

REACTION CONDITIONS FOR α, β-UNSATURATED COMPOUNDS BY THE BROMINE-BROMIDE METHOD

Compound	Reaction Conditions	
	Saponification Time, min.	Bromination Time, min.[a]
Acrylic acid	—	5
Butyl acrylate	5	5
Cellosolve acrylate	15	5
Crotonic acid	—	5
Dibutyl fumarate	45[b]	45[c,d]
Dibutyl maleate	45[b]	30[c]
Diethyl fumarate	30	45[c,d]
Diethyl maleate	30	30[c]
Ethyl acrylate	5	5
Ethyl crotonate	5	5
Fumaric acid	—	45[d]
Maleic acid	—	30
Methacrylic acid	—	15
Methyl methacrylate	30	20

(a) Use a 10 ml. aliquot of sample dilution unless indicated by (c).
(b) Use 10 ml. of acetone as co-solvent.
(c) Use a 15 ml. aliquot of sample dilution.
(d) Omit solid sodium bromide.

This method is particularly useful for determining the unsaturation of maleic and fumaric acids and esters because these compounds are difficult to determine by other unsaturation methods. The method is also capable of good reproducibility. With ethyl acrylate, the standard deviation for 15° of freedom is 0.11.

In general, compounds that interfere in the previously described bromine-bromide method also interfere in this procedure.

Pyridinium Sulfate Dibromide Method

Pyridinium sulfate dibromide $(C_5H_5N \cdot H_2SO_4 \cdot Br_2)$ in glacial acetic acid[7], catalyzed with mercuric acetate[8], is one of the more powerful halogenation reagents. The following method, based upon this reagent, can be used for the determination of the unsaturation of many compounds that cannot be determined readily by other unsaturation methods. For this reason the pyridinium sulfate dibromide method is included in this chapter, even though the method is subject to serious substitutive side reactions.

Reagents. Pyridinium sulfate dibromide, 0.1 N. Add 16 ml. of pyridine to 200 ml. of glacial acetic acid contained in a 2 l. volumetric flask and mix. Add 11 ml. of concentrated sulfuric acid to 100 ml. of glacial acetic acid contained in an Erlenmeyer flask and mix. Slowly add the sulfuric acid solution to the pyridine solution, mix, and cool to room temperature. Add 5.1 ml. of reagent grade bromine to the volumetric flask dilute to volume and mix. Store the solution in a brown bottle. Mercuric acetate solution, 2.5 wt/wt % in glacial acetic acid. Potassium iodide, 15% aqueous solution. Standard 0.1 N sodium thiosulfate.

Procedure. Pipet 50.0 ml. of the pyridinium sulfate dibromide reagent into each of two pressure bottles. Reserve one of the bottles as a blank. Weigh no more than 3.5 m-equiv. of unsaturated compound into the other bottle. Insert the bottles in fabric bags; then add 50 ml. of the mercuric acetate solution. Stopper the bottles, close the tops of the fabric bags and place the bottles in a dark cabinet. Allow the bottles to stand until the bromination reaction is complete (see Table 28). Remove the bottles from the cabinet, remove the fabric bags, and unstopper the bottles. Rapidly add 10 ml. of 15% potassium iodide to each bottle. Add 100 ml. of distilled water to each bottle and titrate with standard 0.1 N sodium thiosulfate to the disappearance of the iodine color. The solution at the end point is a pale yellow, and further addition of titrant will not decolorize the solution.

Scope and Limitations. The pyridinium sulfate dibromide method can be used to determine the unsaturation in many compounds that are quite difficult to brominate. A few compounds that have been determined by the method are listed in Table 28. α, β-Unsaturated compounds can be determined by the method; however, the method is not as satisfactory as the other methods presented in this chapter for these compounds. The method can be used to determine the unsaturation of sorbic acid,

$$CH_3-CH\!=\!CH\!-\!CH\!=\!CH\!-\!\overset{\overset{\displaystyle O}{\|}}{C}\!-\!OH,$$

which contains two double bonds both of which are conjugated to the carboxyl group. The unsaturation in this compound cannot be determined by any other known method.

TABLE 28

REACTION CONDITIONS FOR UNSATURATED COMPOUNDS BY THE PYRIDINIUM SULFATE DIBROMIDE METHOD

Compound	Reaction Time, min.
Allylamine	15
Diallylamine	15
Ethyl acrylate	15
1,5-Hexadiene	5
2,4-Hexadienal	90
Methyl methacrylate	5
Potassium sorbate	120
Sodium vinyl sulfonate	60
Sorbic acid	120

The major disadvantage of this method is the tendency for substitution reactions to occur. These reactions can be inhibited by excluding ultraviolet light, but even under these conditions some substitution occurs, particularly with compounds that contain tertiary carbon atoms. Because of the effect of light on the method, care must be exercised to keep the reaction flasks in the dark during bromination. However, even under carefully controlled conditions, the reproducibility of the method is no better than ± 0.5 per cent because of side reactions.

Interferences due to oxidative side reactions do not appear to be any worse than with the bromine-bromide reagents, the major source of difficulty arising from aldehydes, secondary alcohols, peroxides, and inorganic reducing agents.

Wijs Method

A solution of iodine monochloride in glacial acetic acid, Wijs reagent[9] is the accepted reagent for determining unsaturation in natural oils[1]. The reagent is prepared by dissolving iodine in glacial acetic acid and passing gaseous chlorine through the solution until the halogen content exactly doubles. Although the reagent is difficult to prepare, and the method has little use except for analyzing natural oils, the method is included in this chapter because of the importance of that use.

Reagents. Iodine monochloride, 0.2 N in acetic acid. Dissolve 13 g of resublimed iodine in 1000 ml. of glacial acetic acid. Cool and remove 200 ml. of the solution. Pass dry chlorine gas into the remainder of the solution until the halogen content doubles, as determined by adding potassium iodide to an aliquot of the solution and titrating the liberated iodine with 0.1 N sodium thiosulfate. The color of the reagent also undergoes a change when the correct amount of chlorine has been added and this can be used as a guide in the preparation of the reagent. If an excess of chlorine is present in the solution, adjust the reagent by adding the iodine solution previously reserved. Store the reagent in a brown bottle.
Potassium iodide, 15% aqueous solution.
Standard 0.1 N sodium thiosulfate.
Starch indicator, 1% solution.

Procedure. Add 20 ml. of reagent-grade carbon tetrachloride to two 500-ml. glass-stoppered Erlenmeyer flasks. Reserve one of the flasks as a blank. Weigh no more than 2.5 m-equiv. of unsaturated compound into the other flask. Pipet 25.0 ml. of the iodine monochloride reagent into each flask and quickly place the flasks in a dark cabinet for 30 min. Remove the flasks from the cabinet, add 10 ml. of 15% potassium iodide and 100 ml. of distilled water. Immediately titrate with standard 0.1 N sodium thiosulfate using starch indicator.

Scope and Limitations. As previously mentioned, the Wijs method is the standard method for the determination of the unsaturation of natural oils and the procedure is entirely adequate for this purpose.

The method cannot be used for determining the unsaturation of conjugated dienes or α, β-unsaturated compounds. The former compounds should be determined by the pyridinium sulfate dibromide method while the latter compounds, depending upon their structure, can be determined by the pyridinium sulfate dibromide, bromine-bromide, or the morpholine (discussed subsequently) methods.

Substitution occurs readily with the Wijs reagent and the reaction must be conducted in the dark to inhibit this interference. Even under this condition, substitution can be serious, particularly with compounds that contain a hydrogen atom bonded to a tertiary carbon atom. Because of this and the other limitations discussed, the method should be restricted to the analysis of natural oils.

MORPHOLINE METHOD

α, β-Unsaturated compounds react readily with nucleophilic reagents because the strong electron-withdrawing group induces a partial positive charge on the β-carbon atom:

$$\text{CH}_2\!=\!\overset{\frown}{\text{CH}}\underset{\delta+}{-}\overset{\displaystyle \overset{O^{\delta-}}{\underset{\|}{}}}{\text{C}}\!-\!\text{OR}$$

The β-carbon atom is, therefore, susceptible to attack by electronegative reagents and this principle has been used as the basis for methods for determining this class of unsaturation.

The nucleophilic reagent morpholine, a secondary amine, reacts quantitatively with many α, β-unsaturated compounds to form the corresponding tertiary amine[3].

$$\text{O S NH}(xs) + \text{CH}_2\!=\!\text{CH}\!-\!\text{X} \rightarrow \text{O S NCH}_2\text{CH}_2\!-\!\text{X}$$

The method described here is a modification of the original procedure of Critchfield, Johnson, and Funk[3]. In the method, an excess of morpholine is used, and the reaction is catalyzed with acetic acid in some cases to obtain quantitative reactions. After the reaction is complete the excess morpholine is acetylated in methyl Cellosolve medium, and the tertiary amine is titrated with standard perchloric acid in methyl Cellosolve, using a screened thymol blue indicator. Under the conditions of the titration, the amides formed from excess morpholine and acetic acid are neutral and do not interfere in the titration.

Reagents. Morpholine, Union Carbide Chemicals Co., commercial grade.

Methanol.

Methyl Cellosolve, Union Carbide Chemicals Co., commercial grade.

Acetic anhydride, 99%.

Acetic acid, 50 v/v % aqueous solution.

Perchloric acid, 0.5 N in methyl Cellosolve. Prepare from 70 to 72% perchloric acid and standardize against tris(hydroxymethyl)aminomethane (Fisher certified reagent) in water using 0.1% bromocresol green indicator

Thymol blue-xylene cyanol mixed indicator. Dissolve 0.3 g of thymol blue and 0.08 g of xylene cyanol FF in 100 ml. of dimethylformamide.

Procedure. Add 10 ml. of morpholine to each of two Erlenmeyer flasks, or heat-resistant pressure bottles if the reaction is conducted at 98°C. Reserve one of the flasks as a blank. Weigh no more than 15 m-equiv. of unsaturated compound into the other flask. Add 10 ml. of methanol or 7 ml. of the acetic aciol solution if the reaction requires catalysis (see Table 29). If elevated temperatures are required, insert the pressure bottles in fabric bags, stopper the bottles, and place them in a steam bath at $98 \pm 2°C$. Allow the flasks to stand for sufficient time to obtain quantitative reaction (see Table 29). Allow the flasks to cool, add 50 ml. of methyl Cellosolve, and slowly add 20 ml. of acetic anhydride. Allow the flasks to cool to room temperature. Add 6 to 8 drops of the mixed indicator and titrate with the 0.5 N perchloric acid to the disappearance of the green color.

Scope and Limitations. Unsaturated compounds that have the following structure can be determined by the morpholine method:

$$H_2C{=}CH{-}X$$

where X can be $-\overset{\overset{\displaystyle O}{\displaystyle \|}}{C}OH$, SO_3H, $-\overset{\overset{\displaystyle O}{\displaystyle \|}}{C}NH_2$, $-\overset{\overset{\displaystyle O}{\displaystyle \|}}{C}OR$, or $-C{\equiv}N$. The nature of the electron-withdrawing group has a dominant effect upon the rate of reaction with morpholine and the relative rates increase roughly in the same order as given above. If X is $-\overset{\overset{\displaystyle O}{\displaystyle \|}}{C}-H$, $-\overset{\overset{\displaystyle O}{\displaystyle \|}}{C}-R$, or $-\overset{\overset{\displaystyle O}{\displaystyle \|}}{C}-ONa$, the unsaturated compound reacts slowly with morpholine and cannot be determined. Substitution of an alkyl group on either the α, or β-carbon atoms retards the rate of reaction and the rate is inversely proportional to the length of the alkyl chain. Compounds that are substituted at both the α and β position, even with methyl groups, cannot be determined. Fortunately, compounds that react too slowly with morpholine to be determined by this method brominate readily and can be determined in this manner.

TABLE 29

REACTION CONDITIONS FOR DETERMINING α,β-UNSATURATED COMPOUNDS BY THE MORPHOLINE METHOD

Compound	Reaction Conditions		
	Catalyst or co-solvent	Time, min.	Temp., °C
Acrylamide	Acetic acid	5	25
Acrylic acid	Acetic acid	15	98
Acrylonitrile	Methanol	5	25
Allyl cyanide	Acetic acid	60	98
Crotonitrile	Acetic acid	30	98
Ethyl acrylate	Methanol	5	25
Ethyl crotonate	Acetic acid	15	98
2-Ethylhexyl acrylate	Methanol	5	25
2-Ethylhexyl crotonate	Acetic acid	15	98
Methacrylonitrile	Acetic acid	120	98
Methyl methacrylate	Acetic acid	45	98
Tridecyl acrylate	Methanol	5	25
Vinyl sulfone	Methanol	5	25

In general, morpholine will not react with unsaturated compounds that are not conjugated to a strong electron-withdrawing group. The one known exception to this is allyl cyanide which isomerizes to crotonitrile under the conditions of the reaction:

$$CH_2=CHCH_2C\equiv N \longrightarrow CH_3CH=CHC\equiv N$$

The method is not readily applicable to the determination of maleic and fumaric acids and their esters, because the tertiary amino nitrogen formed is α to the carboxyl group and is, therefore, a weak base. These compounds can be determined by the modification of the bromine-bromide method previously discussed.

Because the method is based upon an acid-base titration, it is subject to interference from acidic and basic constituents present in the sample. Acids with ionization constants in water greater than

2×10^{-2}, tertiary amines, and strong inorganic bases, interfere quantitatively and a correction can be applied.

Many epoxides react quantitatively with the reagent to form tertiary amines, which are also basic under the conditions of the titration. A method for determining epoxides based on this reaction is presented in the chapter on 1,2-epoxy compounds.

Large quantities of aldehydes, ketones, and anhydrides, may interfere by depleting the reagent. α,β-Unsaturated aldehydes may interfere by forming tertiary amines. Organic halides react with morpholine to liberate halogen acids and cannot be tolerated.

MERCURIC ACETATE METHOD

Several reagents other than halogenation reagents have been proposed for the determination of unsaturated compounds. One such reagent, morpholine, was discussed previously. Usually these reagents, are limited in applicability to a select class of compounds. However, one reagent with fairly general applicability is mercuric acetate.

Mercuric acetate reacts with unsaturated compounds in methanol to produce mercury addition compounds with the formation of one mole of acetic acid. In accordance with Markownikoff's rule, mercury bonds to the carbon atom having the most hydrogen atoms.

$$\underset{\substack{\\ \\ }}{R-CH=CH_2 + CH_3OH + Hg(O-\overset{\overset{\displaystyle O}{\|}}{C}-CH_3)_2} \longrightarrow$$

$$\underset{\substack{| \\ CH_3OCHCH_2HgOCCH_3}}{\overset{R}{}\ \ \overset{\overset{\displaystyle O}{\|}}{}\ \ \overset{\overset{\displaystyle O}{\|}}{}} + CH_3COH$$

In the method presented here[5], the acetic acid formed is titrated with standard methanolic potassium hydroxide using phenolphthalein indicator. Since acetic acid cannot be titrated in the presence of excess of mercuric acetate because of the formation of mercuric oxide, sodium bromide is added to convert the mercuric acetate to mercuric bromide, which does not interfere in the titration.

Reagents. Mercuric acetate, 0.12 M in methanol. Add sufficient acetic acid to the reagent so that 50 ml. of the reagent will give a titration of 1 to 10 ml. with 0.1 N methanolic potassium hydroxide using phenolphthalein indicator.

Standard 0.1 N potassium hydroxide in methanol.

Phenolphthalein indicator, 1.0% solution in methanol.

Sodium bromide, reagent grade.

Procedure. Pipet 50.0 ml. of the reagent into each of two Erlenmeyer flasks. Reserve one of the flasks as a blank. Cool the flasks to the desired temperature if the reaction is to be conducted at reduced temperature. Weigh no more than 4 m-equiv. of unsaturated compound into one of the flasks. Allow the flasks to stand at the optimum temperature and for sufficient time to obtain quantitative reaction (see Table 30). Do not use dry ice for cooling the flasks. Add 2 to 4 g of sodium bromide to each flask. Titrate the contents of each flask with the standard potassium hydroxide using phenolphthalein indicator. Note: If the reaction was conducted at −10°C, do not allow the temperature of the solution to exceed 15°C during the titration.

TABLE 30

REACTION CONDITIONS FOR DETERMINING UNSATURATED COMPOUNDS BY THE MERCURIC ACETATE METHOD

Compounds	Reaction Conditions	
	Temp., °C	Time, min.
Allyl acetate	25	60
Allyl acetone	−10	20
Allyl alcohol	25	1
Cyclohexene	25	1
2,5-Dimethyl-1,5-hexadirene	25	15
3,4-Epoxy-1-butene	25	60
2-Ethoxy-3,4-dihydropyran	0	30
2-Formyl-3,4-dihydropyran	25	30
4-Methyl-1-pentene	25	40
2-Methylstyrene	−10	5
1-Propenyl ethyl ether	−10	10
Styrene	25	10
Vinyl acetate(a)	25	10
Vinyl allyl ether	−10	10
Vinyl butyl ether	−10	10
Vinyl ethyl ether	−10	10
N-Vinylpyrrolidone	25	10

(a) Vinyl acetate consumes two equivalents of potassium hydroxide because of saponification during titration.

Scope and Limitations. The mercuric acetate method is valuable for determining the unsaturation of vinyl compounds. $CH_2=$ $CH—$, particularly vinyl ethers. The method is more or less restricted to compounds that contain terminal or isolated unsaturation. For unsaturated compounds that are branched at one of the unsaturated carbon atoms, the method is applicable only to the *cis* isomers. In general, sterically hindered compounds do not react readily with the reagent.

This method is simple to apply and is capable of excellent reproducibility. The method can be applied in many cases where halogenation methods fail, because of substitution reactions or interferences from reducing agents.

α, β-Unsaturated acids, aldehydes, esters, ketones, and nitriles do not react quantitatively by the method. Conjugated dienes also cannot be determined. Inorganic anions, especially halides, must be absent because they react with mercuric ion to deplete the reagent. Because the method is based upon an acid-base titration, the sample must be neutral to phenolphthalein indicator or a suitable correction applied.

Large quantities of water can interfere in the method by hydrolyzing the mercury addition product. For this reason best results are obtained with anhydrous samples. Easily saponified esters such as formates can interfere in the method; however, this type of interference can be inhibited by cooling the samples during the titration. One unsaturated ester, vinyl acetate, is quantitatively saponified during the titration at room temperature, therefore, consuming two equivalents of potassium hydroxide.

SILVER PERCHLORATE METHOD

Acetylinic compounds are normally determined by methods that are based upon the reaction with the acidic hydrogen attached to one of the electron-deficient carbon atoms. One of the more useful methods of this type is based upon the reaction of acetylinic compounds with silver perchlorate in methanol [2]:

$$HC{=}CH + 2AgClO_4 \longrightarrow HC{\equiv}CAg \cdot AgClO_4 + HClO_4$$

The liberated perchloric acid is titrated with standard tris (hydroxy-methyl)aminomethane in methanol, using a screened thymol blue indicator. Since the method is based upon the reaction with an acidic hydrogen, the method naturally is not applicable to disubstituted acetylenes.

Reagents. Silver perchlorate, anhydrous; G. Frederick Smith Chemical Company, Columbus, Ohio.

Standard 0.1 N tris (hydroxymethyl) aminomethane in methanol. Prepare from Fisher Certified Reagent and standardize against standard aqueous hydrochloric acid using bromocresol green indicator.

Thymol blue-alphazurin mixed indicator. Dissolve 0.1 mg of thymol blue and 0.025 g of alphazurin in 100 ml. of methanol. The indicator is stable for two weeks. Note: Alphazurin can be purchased from General Laboratory Supply Co., P. O. Box 2607, Patterson, New Jersey.

Procedure. Add 20 ml. of methanol to an Erlenmeyer flask. Add 2 g of silver perchlorate and dissolve. Add 3 drops of the mixed indicator and neutralize the solution with the standard 0.1 N tris(hydroxymethyl)aminomethane. Weigh no more than 3 m-equiv. of acetylinic compound into the flask. Titrate with the standard 0.1 N tris(hydroxymethyl)aminomethane to a green end point.

Scope and Limitations. The silver perchlorate method is applicable to most mono-substituted acetylinic compounds. The method is particularly valuable for determining these compounds in the presence of easily saponifiable esters and weak acids, since nonaqueous conditons are employed and a low-pH indicator is used for the titration. As mentioned previously, di-substituted acetylenes cannot be determined by the method.

Because the method is based upon an acid-base titration, samples that are not neutral to the indicator interfere. This difficulty can usually be eliminated by prior neutralization of the sample or by applying a correction.

Large quantities of solvents of low dielectric constant can interfere by inhibiting the ionic reaction between silver perchlorate and the acetylene. This problem can be minimized by increasing the volume of methanol solvent. Water may interfere with the indicator end point, but again this problem can be minimized by increasing the volume of methanol.

Materials that complex with silver ion may interfere by inhibiting the reaction. Solvents that are known to interfere in this manner include, acetonitrile (1.0 g), dimethylformamide (2.5 g), and dimethyl sulfoxide (5.0 g).

SUMMARY

The bromine-bromide method of Kaufmann is applicable to a wide variety of olefinic unsaturated compounds, and is an excellent method because substitution reactions are minimized. The method is not directly applicable to the determination of α, β-unsaturated nitriles, acids, and esters; however, the latter compounds can be determined by the method, if they are converted to the alkali metal salts by neutralization or saponification. The pyridinium sulfate dibromide reagent is one of the more reactive halogenation reagents, and can be used to determine the unsaturation of many compounds that cannot be determined by other methods. The major objection to the method is the tendency for substitution reactions to occur. The Wijs method has been used with considerable success for the analysis of natural oils but has little applicability outside of this field.

Reagents other than halogens that are useful are morpholine, mercuric acetate, and silver perchlorate. The morpholine method is useful for determining α, β-unsaturated nitriles, esters, and acids. The method can be used for those α, β-unsaturated compounds that cannot be converted to the alkali metal salts of acids. For a non-halogen reagent, the mercuric acetate reagent is applicable to many unsaturated compounds. The method is useful for determining terminal and isolated unsaturated compounds in the presence of materials that interfere in the halogen methods. Mono-substituted acetylinic compounds are normally determined by reactions based upon their acidic hydrogens, and silver perchlorate is an excellent reagent for this purpose.

REFERENCES

1. Association of Official Agricultural Chemists, *Official Methods of Analysis*, pp. 464, 8th ed., Washington, 1955.
2. BARNES, L., Jr., *Anal. Chem.*, 31, 405 (1959).

3. CRITCHFIELD, F. E., FUNK, G. L., JOHNSON, J. B., *Anal. Chem.*, **28**, 76 (1958).
4. CRITCHFIELD, F. E., JOHNSON, J. B., *Anal. Chem,,* **31**, 1406 (1959).
5. JOHNSON, J. B., FLETCHER, J. P., *Anal. Chem.*, 1563 (1954).
6. KAUFMANN, H. P., *Z. Untersuch. Lebensm.*, **51**, 3 (1926).
7. ROSENMUND, K. W., KUHMHENN, W., ROSENBERG-GRUSZYNSKI, D., RO- SETTI, H., *Z. Untersuch. Nahr. u. Genussm.*, **46**, 154 (1923).
8. ROWE, G., FURNAS, C. C., BLISS, H., *Ind. Eng. Chem., Anal. Ed.*, **16**, 371 (1944).
9. WIJS, J. J. A., *Ber.* **31**, 750 (1898).

CHAPTER 7

1,2-EPOXY COMPOUNDS

BECAUSE of the reactivity of the oxirane oxygen ring, 1,2-epoxides can be determined by reaction with a wide variety of nucleophilic reagents. The reagents commonly employed for these compounds react with the oxirane oxygen ring in the following manner:

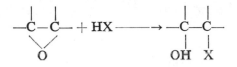

In this equation X represents a nucleophilic radical. Among the reagents that have been successfully used for the determination of 1,2-epoxides are the hydrogen acids, particularly the hydrogen halides, and amines.

The classical method for epoxy compounds was developed by Lubatti [8,9] and is based upon the reaction with aqueous hydrochloric acid saturated with magnesium chloride. The desired reaction is the formation of the chlorohydrin, and the excess chloride ion in the reagent inhibits the hydrolysis of the epoxide to the corresponding glycol.

Although the Lubatti method, or modifications of it, have been used successfully for years for ethylene and propylene oxides, the method is limited to water soluble, very reactive, epoxides and is, therefore, not of general applicability. For this reason, a detailed discussion of the method is not included in this chapter.

In general, the difficulties encountered in determining epoxides with nucleophilic reagents can be traced to one of the following:

1. Side reactions of the epoxide or its reaction product with components in the reagent.
2. Lack of reactivity.

3. Lack of solubility.

4. Interferences in the sample.

The side reaction that causes the most difficulty is ring-opening by the solvent (or traces of water) catalyzed by the nucleophilic reagent. This type of side-reaction usually occurs only with the more reactive epoxides.

The second most prevalent side reaction is the acid-catalyzed isomerization of the epoxide to the corresponding aldehyde. This reaction occurs as shown in the following equation, and with epoxides of the structure indicated:

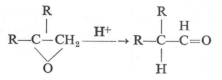

Usually only epoxides containing a tertiary carbon atom undergo this type of isomerization; however, styrene oxide,

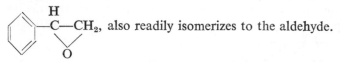 also readily isomerizes to the aldehyde.

These side reactions and the other factors that affect the applicability of the methods will be discussed in more detail in the sections devoted to the description of the specific methods.

The methods discussed in this chapter are based upon the reaction of the epoxides with hydrogen bromide, pyridine hydrochloride, and morpholine (a secondary amine). Also, a colorimetric method for determining trace concentrations of epoxides is discussed. The methods presented were selected because of their general applicability, or because they satisfy a specific need not covered by the more general methods.

INDIRECT HYDROGEN BROMIDE METHOD

In glacial acetic acid medium, hydrogen bromide reacts rapidly and completely with a wide variety of 1,2-epoxides to form the corresponding bromohydrin. This reaction has been used as the basis of probably the most generally applicable of the methods developed to date for determining oxirane oxygen compounds [7]. In the procedure described here, a measured excess of the hydrogen bromide in acetic acid is reacted with the sample and the unreacted hydrogen bromide is titrated with standard sodium acetate in acetic acid using crystal violet indicator.

Reagents. Glacial acetic acid, Grasselli reagent grade or equivalent.

Hydrogen bromide, approximately 0.5 N in glacial acetic acid. Add 67 ml. of reagent-grade bromide to 2 l. of glacial acetic acid. Add reagent-grade phenol in 10 g increments until the solution becomes light straw in color (approximately 100 g) and add 10 g in excess. Mix the solution after each addition of phenol and allow to stand for 12 hr before using.

Standard 0.2 N sodium acetate in glacial acetic acid. Standardize against 0.1 N perchloric acid in glacial acetic acid using crystal violet indicator.

Crystal violet indicator, 1.0% solution in glacial acetic acid.

Procedure. Pressure pipet 25.0 ml. of the hydrogen bromide solution into two iodine flasks. Reserve one of the flasks as a blank. Weigh approximately 6 m-equiv. of 1,2-epoxide into the other flask. Stopper the flasks and use 5 ml. of glacial acetic acid as a liquid seal for the iodine flasks. Allow the sample to react for sufficient time to obtain quantitative reaction. Minimum reaction times for a few epoxides are listed in Table 31. Remove the stoppers, wash down the inside walls of the flasks with 25 ml. of glacial acetic acid. Add 5 to 6 drops of crystal violet indicator to each flask and titrate the contents with the standard 0.2 N sodium acetate to the appearance of the first blue-green color.

Scope and Limitations. The hydrogen bromide in acetic acid method is applicable to a wide variety of 1,2-epoxy compounds, a few of which are shown in Table 31. The reagent is the most reactive of all epoxide reagents and most compounds react quantitatively in less than 15 minutes at room temperature. Epoxides that cannot be determined by this method generally react rapidly with the reagent but undergo complicating side reactions.

1,2-epoxy compounds that acid hydrolyze to aldehydes can not usually be determined by this method. Compounds in this category include styrene oxide, and epoxides in which the oxirane oxygen is attached to a tertiary carbon atom.

Low results may be obtained with epoxides that undergo rapid acid-catalyzed ring-opening. An example of such a compound

TABLE 31

DETERMINATION OF 1,2-EPOXIDES BY THE HYDROGEN BROMIDE IN
ACETIC ACID METHOD

Compound	Structure	Reaction Time, min. at 25°C	No. of Reacting Groups
1,2,3,4-Diepoxybutane	CH_2—CH—CH—CH_2 _O_/ _O_/	15	2
Epichlorohydrin	$ClCH_2CH$—CH_2 _O_/	15	1
1,2-Epoxy-3-butene	H H H_2C—C—C=CH_2 _O_/	30	1
2,3-Epoxy-3-butene	H H_3C—C—C=CH_2 _O_/	60	1
Epoxycyclohexane	CH_2 H / \ C CH_2 O<	 C CH_2 H \ / CH_2	60	1
Ethylene oxide	CH_2—CH_2 _O_/	15	1
Propylene oxide	CH_2CH—CH_3 _O_/	15	1
Soybean oil epoxide	—	15	
Vinylcyclohexane dioxide	CH_2 H / \ H C C-CH-CH_2 O< _O_/ C CH_2 H \ / CH_2	15	2

is dicyclopentadiene dioxide. In this case, ring-opening by the acetic acid solvent occurs simultaneously with the desired reaction to form the bromohydrin:

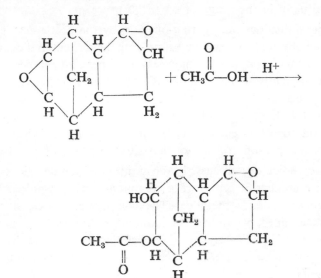

The oxirane oxygen on the five-membered ring reacts quantitatively with hydrogen bromide, while the ring containing the endomethylene group undergoes the side reaction [5]. Other epoxy compounds containing the endomethylene group behave similarily.

Another epoxy compound that undergoes this side reaction with the solvent is 3,4-epoxy-6-methylcyclohexylmethyl-3,4-epoxy 6-methylcyclohexane carboxylate:

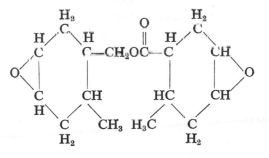

With this particular compound results are usually 2 to 4 per cent low, while in the case of dicyclopentadiene dioxide the side-reaction is more extensive, and results for purity determinations are usually in the range of 65 to 70 per cent.

The difficulties due to ring-opening by the acetic acid solvent can be obviated somewhat by preparing the reagent in dioxane [10]. With this reagent, purities in excess of 95 per cent can be obtained with dicyclopentadiene dioxide, the results being dependent upon the water content of the reagent. The usefulness of this reagent is limited because of its inherent instability. Hydrogen bromide tends to cleave dioxane, and the extent of the reaction is inversely proportional to the water content of the reagent.

The difficulties discussed above in determining the oxirane oxygen content of certain ring compounds are not unique to the hydrogen bromide methods. The compounds discussed cannot be determined by any of the other standard epoxide methods, because of acid-catalyzed ring-opening from active hydrogen (other than the reagent) or because of non-reactivity with basic reagents.

Because of the reactivity of hydrogen bromide, this method is subject to interference from a few non-epoxy compounds. Unsaturated compounds that may interfere include conjugated dienes, α, β-unsaturated compounds, and isobutylene. The latter compound reacts quantitatively. 1,2-Glycols and tertiary alcohols react quantitatively provided that sufficient reaction time is allowed as discussed in the chapter on hydroxyl compounds.

Peroxides will react with hydrogen bromide to liberate bromine and consume the reagent. This interference can be eliminated by incorporating an excess of phenol into the reagent to react with the bromine to regenerate hydrogen bromide [1]. The net effect of this reaction sequence is a consumption of one mole of hydrogen bromide per mole of peroxide, thus allowing a correction to be made.

Most amines or stronger bases interfere quantitatively in the method and can be corrected for. Acids stronger than nitric also interfere quantitatively.

Water and other hydroxylic solvents interfere, as in other nonaqueous titration methods employing glacial acetic acid medium. Usually up to 0.5 per cent water can be present in the titration medium without seriously affecting the end point, while somewhat higher concentrations of alcohols can be tolerated.

DIRECT HYDROGEN BROMIDE METHOD

Many 1,2-epoxy compounds react practically instantaneously with hydrogen bromide in acetic acid and can, therefore, be titrated directly with this reagent [4]. This procedure is particularly useful for circumventing interferences encountered with the indirect procedure in which an excess of hydrogen bromide is employed.

In the procedure described here 1,2-epoxides are titrated directly with standard hydrogen bromide in acetic acid using crystal violet indicator.

Reagents. Glacial acetic acid, Grasselli reagent grade or equivalent.

Chlorobenzene, Technical grade, E.I. du Pont de Nemours and Co., Inc.

Crystal violet indicator, 0.1 per cent solution in acetic acid.

Hydrogen bromide, 0.1 N in glacial acetic acid. Add 6.5 ml. of reagent grade bromide to 1 l. of glacial acetic acid. Add reagent grade phenol in 1.0 g increments until the solution becomes light straw in color (approx. 10 g) and add 1 g in excess. Mix the solution after each addition of phenol and allow to stand for 12 hr. Standardize against Bureau of Standards potassium acid phthalate in acetic acid using crystal violet indicator.

Appratus. Reservoir buret, Karl Fischer Type, Arthur H. Thomas Co., No. 2484-B. Draw the buret tip to a finer bore. Fill the drying tubes of the reservoir and buret with anhydrous sodium sulfate. Replace the drying tube of the reservoir with a ball joint stopper when the buret is not in use.

A No. 3 rubber stopper with a hole just large enough to accommodate the buret tip. Make a groove in the side of the stopper to allow escape of replaced air during titration.

Procedure. Add 5 ml. of chlorobenzene to a 50-ml. Erlenmeyer flask. Weigh 2.2 m-equiv. of 1,2-epoxy compound into the flask. Add 5 drops of crystal violet indicator to the flask. Insert a Teflon-sealed magnetic stirring bar and connect the flask to the buret assembly with the rubber stopper in position. Stir the solution with a magnetic stirrer and titrate to a blue-green end point permanent for at least one minute. Some of the epoxides react at a relatively slow rate; therefore, as the end point is approached add the titrant in small increments and allow sufficient time to insure that the blue color does not return. For accurate results the reagent must be standardized within an hour of the titration of the sample. Note: The rate of change in normality of the reagent becomes excessive at temperatures above 27°C.

Scope and Limitations. As previously discussed, the indirect hydrogen bromide method is subject to interference from certain non-epoxy compounds. Most of these interferences can be minimized, however, by using the direct titration procedure. Of the interferences discussed only isobutylene, peroxides, strongly

TABLE 32

DETERMINATION OF 1,2-EPOXIDES BY THE DIRECT HYDROGEN
BROMIDE METHOD

Compound	Structure	No. of Reacting Groups
Bis (2,3-epoxycyclopentyl) ether		2
1,2,3,4-Diepoxybutane		2
Ethylene oxide		1
Soybean oil epoxide	—	—
Vinylcyclohexane monoxide		1

acidic, and basic materials interfere in this procedure. The latter three types of interferences can be corrected for.

Because of the great reactivity of hydrogen bromide with epoxy compounds, many 1,2-epoxides react sufficiently fast with the reagent to allow direct titration of these compounds. A few of the compounds that can be determined in this manner are shown in Table 32. In general the compounds listed in Table 31 that require reaction times in excess of 15 min by the indirect procedure react too slowly with the reagent to be determined by the direct procedure. The direct procedure is also subject to the same limitations as the indirect procedure for compounds that acid hydrolyze to aldehydes, or ring-open readily with acidic solvents.

PYRIDINE HYDROCHLORIDE METHOD

Methods based upon the reaction of the oxirane oxygen ring with hydrogen chloride are used more frequently for determining 1,2-epoxides than any of the other procedures. Several solvents have been used for the hydrogen chloride but pyridine has probably received more extensive use[2].

In the modification of the pyridine hydrochloride method described here, an excess of hydrogen chloride in pyridine medium is reacted with the epoxy compound to form the corresponding chlorohydrin. The unreacted hydrogen chloride is titrated with standard base using either phenolphthalein, bromocresol purple, or bromophenol blue indicator. The choice of the indicator used is governed by the stability of the chlorohydrin, and the presence or absence of interferences as will be discussed subsequently.

Reagents. Pyridine hydrochloride solution, approximately 0.5 N. Pass dry hydrogen chloride gas into redistilled pyridine until considerable pyridine hydrochloride has precipitated. Add concentrated hydrochloric acid in small increments until the solid redissolves. Determine the normality by titration with standard strong base. Dilute the reagent with sufficient pyridine to adjust the normality to 0.5.
Standard 0.5 N methanolic potassium hydroxide.
Standardize against Bureau of Standards benzoic acid.

Bromophenol blue indicator, 0.04 per cent solution in pyridine.
Bromocresol purple, 0.15 per cent solution in methanol.
Phenolphthalein, 1.0 per cent solution in pyridine.
Procedure. Pipet 50.0 ml. of the pyridine hydrochloride solution into each of two heat-resistant pressure bottles, reserving one bottle as a blank. Weigh 10 to 15 m-equiv. of 1,2-epoxy compound into the other bottle. Cap the bottles, enclose them in a fabric bag, and place them in a steam bath at $98\pm2°$ for sufficient time to obtain quantitative reaction. The minimum reaction time required for several epoxides is listed in Table 33. Remove the bottle from the bath, cool to room temperature, remove the fabric bags, and uncap the bottles Titrate with standard 0.5 N methanolic potassium hydroxide using the indicator selected for the particular application.

Scope and Limitations. Although the pyridine hydrochloride method is the most commonly used method for 1,2-epoxides, this procedure is not as generally applicable as the hydrogen bromide method. Also, lower results are usually obtained by this method than by the hydrogen bromide method. A few of the many compounds that have been determined by this method are listed in Table 33.

Low results by he pyridine hydrochloride method are usually the result of the hydrolysis of the chlorohydrin by the small amount of water in the reagent. Of course, the usual difficulties due to unreactivity of the epoxide, isomerization of certain epoxides to aldehydes, and undesirable ring-opening with impurities in the reagent also can be responsible for low results.

In order to otain quantitative reaction with epoxides, the reaction with pyridine hydrochloride must be conducted at elevated temperatures for extended periods of time. Under these conditions certain of the chlorohydrins formed hydrolyze with water in the reagent to form the corresponding glycols and liberate hydrogen chloride. Reaction rate studies for relatively unreactive epoxides that form instable chlorohydrins show that the purity values increase to a maximum than decrease with extended reaction time. In such cases the maximum purity value obtained is erroneously low. Epoxy compounds that behave in this manner include soybean oil epoxide, octyl tallate epoxide, and certain epoxy derivatives of cyclohexane. Usually the more reactive epoxides are not subject to this difficulty.

TABLE 33

DETERMINATION OF 1,2-EPOXIDES BY THE PYRIDINE HYDROCHLORIDE
METHOD

Compound	Structure	Minimum Reaction Time, min. at 98°C	No. of Reacting Group
1,2,3,4-Diepoxy-butane	CH_2—CHCH—CH_2 \\/ \\/ O O	30	2
Epichlorohydrin	CH_2—CHCH$_2$Cl \\/ O	45	1
1,2-Epoxybutane	CH_2CHCH$_2$CH$_3$ \\/ O	15	1
1,2-Epoxybutene	CH_2—CH—CH=CH_2 \\/ O	30	1
1,2-Epoxycyclohexane	H$_2$ C H /\ C CH$_2$ O/\ C CH$_2$ H\ C$_2$ H	15	1
Ethylene oxide	CH_2—CH$_2$ \\/ O	30	1
Propylene oxide	CH_2—CHCH$_3$ \\/ O	15	1
Vinylcyclohexane dioxide	H$_2$ C H /\ H H C C—C——CH$_2$ O/\ \\/ O C CH$_2$ H\ C H$_2$	30	2

The pyridine hydrochloride method is less subject to interferences from unsaturated compounds than is the indirect hydrogen
bromide method. Also, the method is considerably less affected
by 1,2-glycols and tertiary alcohols.

Most carboxylic acids interfere quantitatively in the method if
phenolphthalein is used as the indicator. However, when this
indicator is used basic hydrolysis of the chlorohydrins may occur.
This difficulty can be obviated by using bromocresol purple indicator; however, carboxylic acids are not titrated quantitatively
under these conditions (approx. 75 per cent neutralization is
obtained). Bromophenol blue indicator can be used for the
titration of the excess hydrogen chloride in order to minimize
interference from carboxylic acids. Using this indicator, carboxylic acids interfere to the extent of approximately 10 per cent.
Therefore, this indicator can be used when small amounts (less
than 2 per cent) of carboxylic acids are present and corrections
for the acidity of the sample are not necessary.

MORPHOLINE METHOD

Certain relatively reactive 1,2-epoxy compounds react quantitatively with an excess of morpholine to form the corresponding
tertiary amine[6]:

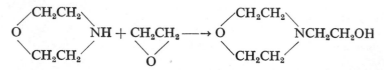

The excess of morpholine is acetylated with acetic anhydride
to form the corresponding amide. The tertiary amine is titrated
with perchloric acid in methyl Cellosolve medium using thymol
blue-xylene cyanol mixed indicator. Under these conditions the
amide and acetic acid formed as a result of the acetylation are
essentially neutral.

Reagents. Standard 0.5 N perchloric acid in methyl Cellosolve. Standardize against tris(hydroxymethyl)aminomethane (Fisher certified reagent) in water using a 0.1 per cent solution of bromocresol green in methanol.

Morpholine, Union Carbide Chemicals Co. commercial grade or equivalent.

Acetic anhydride, Union Carbide Chemicals Co. commercial grade or equivalent.

Methyl Cellosolve, Union Carbide Chemicals Co. commercial grade or equivalent.

Thymol blue-xylene cyanol mixed indicator. Dissolve 0.3 g of thymol blue and 0.08 g of xylene cyanol FF in dimethylformamide.

Methanol, reagent grade.

Procedure. Add 10 ml. of morpholine to each of two heat-resistant pressure bottles. Reserve one as a blank. Add 10 ml. of methanol to each bottle. Weigh approximately 15 m-equiv. of 1,2-epoxy compound into one of the bottles. Wrap the bottles in a fabric bag and place them in a steam bath for sufficient time to give quantitative reaction. Minimum reaction times for a few epoxides are listed in Table 34. Cool the bottles to room temperature, remove the fabric bags, and uncap the bottles. Add 50 ml. of methyl Cellosolve to each bottle. Slowly add 20 ml. of acetic anhydride to each bottle and allow the contents to cool to room temperature. Add 4 to 6 drops of the thymol blue-xylene cyanol mixed indicator and titrate with the standard perchloric acid to the disappearance of the green color.

TABLE 34

DETERMINATION OF 1,2-EPOXIDES BY REACTION WITH MORPHOLINE

Compound	Structure	Minimum Reaction Time, min. at 98°C
1,2-Epoxybutane	CH_2—$CHCH_2CH_3$ \ / O	60
1,2-Epoxybutene	CH_2—$CHCH$=CH_2 \ / O	60
Ethylene oxide	CH_2—CH_2 \ / O	30
Isobutylene oxide	CH_3 \ C—CH_2 / \ / CH_3 O	90
Propylene oxide	CH_2—$CHCH_3$ \ / O	30
Styrene oxide	—$CHCH_2$ \ / O	30

Scope and Limitations. The morpholine method for 1,2-epoxy compounds is limited to the more reactive epoxides. A few of the compounds that can be determined by this method are listed in Table 34. Since basic conditions are prevalent throughout the reaction, isomerization of epoxides to aldehydes is not a problem with this method. The more reactive tertiary epoxides can be determined by this method.

This method is useful for determining epoxides that cannot be determined by the other methods, eg. styrene oxide. The method can also be used to circumvent interferences encountered in the other procedure.

As discussed elsewhere in this book, many α, β-unsaturated compounds react quantitatively by this procedure. Anhydrides and aldehydes react to consume the reagent. Tertiary amines, strong bases, and acids with $pK_a(H_2O)$ less than 3.0 interfere but can usually be corrected for.

COLORIMETRIC METHOD

The procedures previousy discussed for determining 1,2-epoxy compounds are not generally applicable to the determination of trace concentrations of these compounds, because they lack the desired sensitivity.

The colorimetric procedure described here is quite sensitive and can be used for trace analyses[3]. The method is based upon the commonly known fact that 1,2-epoxy compounds can be hydrolyzed to the corresponding glycol in the presence of mineral acid and at elevated temperatures. Cleavage of the 1,2-glycol to formaldehyde is effected by reaction with sodium periodate. The formaldehyde formed is determined colorimetrically by the chromotropic acid method.

Reagents. Sodium chromotropate (sodium 1,8-dihydroxynaphthalene-3, 6-disulfonate); practical grade, Eastman Organic Chemicals Sodium sulfite; 5.5 per cent solution. Prepare fresh reagent at least once every week.
Sodium periodate, 0.1 M.
Procedure. Add the sample, containing an amount of 1,2-epoxy compound equivalent to no more than 0.7 mg of formaldehyde, to a heat-resistant pressure

bottle. Add sufficient distilled water so that the total volume of water in the bottle is at least 10 ml. Add the same total volume of water to a second bottle to be used for the blank. Add 1 ml. of 0.5 N sulfuric acid to each bottle. Cap the bottles, protecting the rubber gaskets with polyethylene film. Enclose the bottles in fabric bags and place them in a steam bath at 98°C for 60 min (longer hydrolysis times may be required for higher molecular weight epoxides). Cool the bottles to room temperature, uncap and remove the fabric bags. Quantitatively transfer the contents of each bottle to 100-ml. glass-stoppered graduated cylinders. Add 1.0 ml. of 0.5 N sodium hydroxide to each cylinder. Pipet 2.0 ml. of the 0.1 N sodium periodate into each cylinder and allow a 60 minute reaction time. Pipet 2.0 ml. of the sodium sulfite solution into each cylinder and dilute to 100 ml. with distilled water.

Transfer 10 ml. aliquots of each dilution to 100-ml. graduated cylinders. Add 0.05 g of sodium chromotropate to each cylinder and dissolve. Dilute to 50 ml. with concentrated sulfuric acid and allow the normal heat rise to occur. Immerse a 20 ml. pipet or capillary tube into each cylinder. Connect the pipet to a nitrogen source and vigorously ebullate for 10 min. Allow the contents to cool to room temperature and measure the absorbance of the sample versus the blank at 570 mμ using 1 cm cells. Read the concentration of 1,2-epoxy compound from a calibration curve prepared using the 1,2-epoxy compound being determined.

Scope and Limitations. This method has been applied to the determination of only ethylene and propylene oxides. However, the method should also be applicable to other 1,2-epoxy compounds that can be acid hydrolyzed to the corresponding glycol. Because the end determination is based upon a color reaction of formaldehyde, this aldehyde must be a product of the periodate cleavage. 1,2-epoxy compounds of the following type cannot be determined:

1,2-Glycols and other compounds that cleave with periodate ion to form formaldehyde will interfere in this method. With the volatile epoxides this difficulty can be obviated by separating the epoxide from the sample by volatilization. Interferences are sometimes encountered from large concentrations of organic compounds that discolor in hot concentrated sulfuric acid. Aldehydes are particularly bad in this respect.

SUMMARY

The indirect hydrogen bromide method is more generally applicable to problems involving the determination of 1,2-epoxy compounds than any other method developed to date. However, this procedure is not universally applicable and is subject to certain limitations. Interferences in the indirect method can generally be avoided by using the procedure based upon the direct titration with hydrogen bromide. Certain epoxy compounds that isomerize under acidic condition to form aldehydes cannot be determined by the hydrogen bromide methods, but can be determined by the method based upon reaction with morpholine. None of the volumetric methods is satisfactory for determining trace concentrations of 1,2-epoxides. However, trace concentrations of certain epoxides can be determined by a colorimetric method, based upon the hydrolysis of the epoxy compound to the corresponding glycol, cleavage with periodate ion to form formaldehyde, and colorimetric determination of the formaldehyde.

REFERENCES

1. BERLIN, E. W., JOHNSON, J. B., unpublished data, Union Carbide Chemicals Co., South Charleston, W. Va.
2. BRADLEY, T. F., U. S. Patent 2, 500, 600.
3. CRITCHFIELD, F. E., JOHNSON, J. B., Anal. Chem., 29, 797 (1957).
4. DURBETAKI, A. J., Anal. Chem., 28, 2000 (1956).
5. DURBETAKI, A. J., American Chemical Society Meeting, Atlantic City, N. J., Sept. 1959.
6. FUNK, G. L., unpublished data, Union Carbide Chemicals Co., South Charleston, W. Va.
7. HOGSETT, J. N., unpublished data, Union Carbide Chemicals Co., South Charleston, W. Va.
8. LUBATTI, O. F., J. Soc. Chem. Ind., 51, 36IT (1932).
9. LUBATTI, O. F., J. Soc. Chem. Ind. 54, 424T (1935).
10. McDERMOTT, W. H., CRITCHFIELD, F. E., unpublished data, Union Carbide Chemicals Co., South Charleston, W. Va.

CHAPTER 8

ESTERS

ESTERS undergo very few chemical reactions, under ordinary conditions, because of their chemical stability. These compounds can be acid hydrolyzed to the corresponding alcohols and carboxylic acids, or saponified to the alcohols and the salts of carboxylic acids. The latter reaction is of most analytical significance and three saponification procedures are discussed in this chapter. The conventional saponification with aqueous potassium hydroxide is applicable to most esters, except for those that are chemically quite resistant or very insoluble in water. A modification of this method, in which phenylhydrazine is incorporated into the reagent, is designed for determining esters in the presence of aldehydes or for determining vinyl esters, since these compounds yield aldehydes instead of alcohols upon saponification. The third saponification procedure employs potassium hydroxide in diethylene glycol, and is designed for chemically resistant or water insoluble esters. Low concentrations of esters are conveniently determined by a colorimetric method based upon the formation of the ferric ion complex of the hydroxamic acid derivatives.

SAPONIFICATION WITH AQUEOUS POTASSIUM HYDROXIDE

The conventional method for determining esters is based upon the saponification with a measured excess of potassium hydroxide and the titration of the excess potassium hydroxide using standard acid and phenolphthalein indicator. Many esters are not soluble in the saponification medium and 2-propanol is used as a co-solvent. The procedure described here is a modification of the original saponification method of Koettstorfer[3].

Reagents. Potassium hydroxide, 1 N aqueous solution.
Hydrochloric acid, standard 0.5 N.
2-propanol.
Methanol.
Phenolphthalein indicator, 1% solution in methanol.

Procedure. Pipet 25.0 ml. of the 1 N potassium hydroxide into each of two 250-ml. glass-stoppered Erlenmeyer flasks. Use heat-resistant pressure bottles if the reaction is to be conducted at elevated temperatures. Add the amount of 2-propanol (do not exceed 40 ml.) specified in Table 35. Reserve one of the flasks as a blank. Weigh no more than 15 m-equiv. of ester into the other flask. If a non-homogeneous solution is obtained, add 5 ml. of methanol to each flask. If elevated temperatures are required, insert the pressure bottles in fabric bags and stopper the bottles. Allow the flasks to stand for the time and at the temperature required for quantitative saponification (see Table 35). If a white precipitate develops, add sufficient distilled water to dissolve the salt. Add the same volume of water to the blank. Titrate the

TABLE 35

REACTION CONDITIONS FOR THE SAPONIFICATION OF ESTERS WITH AQUEOUS POTASSIUM HYDROXIDE

Compound	Reaction Conditions		
	2-propanol Co-solvent ml.	Temp., °C	Time, min.
Butyl acetate	15	25	45
2-Butyl acetate	15	98	15
Butyl acrylate	15	25	60
Butyrolactone	—	25	15
Cyclopentenyl acetate	10	25	15
Dibutyl maleate	15	25	45
Didecyl phthalate	40	98	60
Diethyl sulfate	20	98	15
Dimethyl phthalate	20	98	30
Ethyl acetate	—	25	30
Ethyl acetoacetate	—	98	60
Ethyl formate	—	25	15
2-Ethylhexyl acetate	35	98	15
3-Heptyl acetate	35	98	90
Methyl acetate	—	25	15
Methyl methacrylate	15	98	15
4-Methyl-2-pentylacetate	30	98	30
Thiodiglycol diacetate	10	25	15

contents of each flask with standard 0.5 N hydrochloric acid using phenol-phthalein indicator.

Scope and Limitations. This method is applicable to a wide variety of esters, and the reaction conditions for a few are listed in Table 35. The method is not applicable to very high molecular weight esters for solubility reasons. However, the lower phthalate esters can be solubilized by the 2-propanol co-solvent and can be determined.

Ketones interfere only slightly in the method while aldehydes interfere seriously. Therefore, vinyl esters cannot be determined because aldehydes are the product of their saponification. Organic chlorides, nitriles, and amides interfere in the method, particularly if elevated temperatures are used. Because the method is based upon an acid-base end determination, a correction must be applied if the sample is not neutral to phenolphthalein indicator.

SAPONIFICATION IN THE PRESENCE OF PHENYLHYDRAZINE

Aldehydes interfere seriously in saponification methods because they consume alkali metal hydroxides. This type of interference can be eliminated by conducting the saponification in the presence of phenylhydrazine. In this way the aldehydes are converted to the corresponding phenylhydrazones which are stable to bases. This technique can also be used to determine vinyl esters via saponification[1]. Vinyl esters react with potassium hydroxide as follows:

$$
\underset{\substack{\| \\ RCOCH=CH_2}}{O} + KOH \longrightarrow \underset{\substack{\| \\ CH_3C=O}}{\overset{H}{}} + \underset{\substack{\| \\ RCOH}}{O}
$$

Acetaldehyde formed during the saponification will, ordinarily, further consume potassium hydroxide. In the presence of phenyl-hydrazine, the hydrazone is formed preferentially and this side reaction is eliminated.

Reagents. The reagents are the same as in the previous method with the exception of:
Phenylhydrazine, reagent grade. Do not use the reagent if it becomes highly colored.

Procedure. Pipet 25.0 ml. of the 1 N potassium hydroxide into each of two heat-resistant pressure bottles. Add 35 ml. of 2-propanol and 5 ml. of methanol to each bottle. Purge the bottles with nitrogen for 2 minutes. Pipet 5 ml. of phenylhydrazine into each bottle. Reserve one of the bottles as a blank. Weigh no more than 15 m-equiv. of ester into the other bottle. Insert each bottle in a fabric bag and stopper. Allow the bottles to stand for the time and at the temperature required for quantitative reaction (see Table 36 for vinyl esters). Cool the bottles to room temperature and titrate the contents with 0.5 N hydrochloric acid using phenolphthalein indicator.

Scope and Limitations. This procedure is very effective in eliminating the interference of aldehydes in saponification determinations. The method has also been applied to the vinyl esters listed in Table 36. The method is subject to the same solubility limitations as the previously discussed saponification method. Interferences in the method are also the same except for aldehydes and ketones which do not interfere in this method.

TABLE 36

REACTION CONDITIONS FOR DETERMINING VINYL ESTERS BY
SAPONIFICATION IN THE PRESENCE OF PHENYLHYDRAZINE

Compound	Reaction Time, min. at 98°C
Vinyl formate	15[a]
Vinyl acetate	15
Vinyl propionate	15
Vinyl butyrate	60
Vinyl crotonate	30
Vinyl benzoate	60
Vinyl 2-ethylhexanoate	60
Vinyl oleate	30
Vinyl stearate	15

[a] Conduct the saponification at 25°C.

SAPONIFICATION WITH POTASSIUM HYDROXIDE IN DIETHYLENE GLYCOL

Chemically resistant and high molecular weight water insoluble esters cannot be determined in ordinary saponification media. A system consisting of potassium hydroxide in diethylene glycol can be used to determine esters of this type because (1) solubility problems are eliminated and (2) refluxing diethylene glycol (b.p. 245°C) provides a high temperature for the saponification of chemically resistant esters.

The procedure described below is a modification of the method of Shaefer and Balling[4].

Reagents. Potassium hydroxide, 0.5 N in diethylene glycol. Dissolve 33 g of reagent grade potassium hydroxide in 20 ml. of distilled water and dilute to 1 l. with diethylene glycol.
Hydrochloric acid, standard 0.5 N solution.
Phenolphthalein indicator, 1% solution in methanol.

Procedure. Pipet 50.0 ml. of the 0.5 N potassium hydroxide into each of two 300-ml. 24/40 ⚷ Corning alkali-resistant Erlenmeyer flasks. Allow the same drainage time for both flasks. Reserve one of the flasks as a blank. Weigh no more than 15 m-equiv. of ester into the other flask. Add a few glass beads (do not use boiling stones) to each flask and connect the flasks to water-cooled West condensers. Apply heat and allow the contents to reflux for sufficient time to obtain quantitative saponification (see Table 37). Remove the source of heat from the flasks and allow the contents to cool to room temperature. Purge the tops of the condensers with nitrogen, during cooling, to prevent carbon dioxide contamination. Wash down the walls of the condensers with water. Remove the flasks from the condensers and titrate the contents with standard 0.5 N hydrochloric acid using phenolphthalein indicator.

Scope and Limitations. The reaction conditions used in this method are such that most esters can be saponified quantitatively in a reasonable length of time. The method, however, should only be used when necessary, because it requires special equipment and is not as precise as conventional methods. Reaction conditions for a few high molecular weight esters are listed in Table 37.

Large quantities of low-boiling compounds may interfere by reducing the temperature of the refluxing reaction medium. This difficulty can be minimized by increasing the reflux time.

Ketones and, particularly, aldehydes will interfere in the method by consumption of potassium hydroxide. Nitriles, organic chlorides, and amides will interfere and some compounds of the latter two classes can be determined quantitatively by the method. Substances that are not neutral to the indicator will of course interfere unless a correction is made.

TABLE 37

REACTION CONDITIONS FOR THE SAPONIFICATION OF ESTERS WITH
POTASSIUM HYDROXIDE IN DIETHYLENE GLYCOL

Compound	Refluxing Time, min.
Di(2-ethylhexyl) hexahydrophthalate	120
Diisobutyl carbinol acetate	60
2-Ethylbutyl 2-ethylbutyrate	120
2-Ethylhexyl 2-ethyl-2-hexenoate	60
2-Ethylhexyl β-(2-ethylhexyloxy) butyrate	60
Trioctyl phosphate	180
Tributyl phosphate	60 [a]

[a] Add 2 ml. of butanol to both the sample and blank before refluxing.

HYDROXAMIC ACID COLORIMETRIC METHOD

Esters react with hydroxylamine, under alkaline conditions, to form the corresponding hydroxamic acids:

$$\underset{\substack{\| \\ C}}{ROOR'} + NH_2OH \xrightarrow{OH^-} \overset{O}{\overset{\|}{R C}}NHOH + R'OH$$

The hydroxamic acids react with ferric ion to form red colored complexes:

$$\overset{O}{\overset{\|}{R C}}NHOH + 1/nFe^{+3} \longrightarrow R{-}\underset{\substack{\| \\ O}}{C}{-}\underset{\substack{\| \\ O}}{N}{-}H$$
$$\underset{Fe/n}{\diagdown \diagup}$$

This principle has been used as the basis of the following color-imetric method for esters of carboxylic acids[2].

Reagents. Sodium hydroxide, 12.5 wt./vol. % in methanol.
Hydroxylamine hydrochloride, 12.5 wt./vol. % in methanol.
Alkaline hydroxylamine reagent. Mix equal volumes of the 12.5% hydroxylamine hydrochloride and the 12.5% sodium

hydroxide. Filter the solution through No. 42 Whatman
filter paper. The reagent is stable for 4 hours.

Ferric perchlorate, 5 wt./vol.% in ethanol. Dissolve 5 g of
ferric perchlorate (G. F. Smith Chemical Co.) in 10 ml. of
70 to 72% perchloric acid and 10 ml. of water. Dilute to
100 ml. with ethanol. Cool during the dilution to prevent
excessive heating.

Ferric perchlorate, 0.0057M. Pipet 40 ml. of the 5% ferric
perchlorate into a 1 l. volumetric flask. Add 12 ml. of 70
to 72% perchloric acid and dilute to volume with anhydrous
ethanol. Add the ethanol slowly and cool during the dilution.

Procedure. Pipet 5 ml. of an ethanol solution of the ester, containing 1 to
10 mmoles of ester, into a 250-ml. Erlenmeyer flask with a 19 × 22 $ ground-
glass joint. Pipet 5 ml. of anhydrous ethanol into another flask to be used
as a blank. Pipet 3 ml. of the alkaline hydroxylamine reagent into each flask.
Add a boiling stone to each flask and attach water-cooled reflux condensers
to them. Reflux the solution for 5 min. Wash the contents of the flasks into
50-ml. volumetric flasks with the 0.0057M ferric perchlorate reagent. Dilute
to volume with the reagent. Allow the flasks to stand for 10 min then determine
the absorbance of the sample, using 1 cm cells, vs. the blank at the wavelength
of maximum absorbance (approx. 530 mμ). Determine the concentration of
anhydride by reference to a calibration curve prepared from the ester being
determined.

Scope and Limitations. This method is valuable for determining
low (0.05 to 1%) concentrations of esters in non-interfering
solvents. The method has been applied to a wide variety of esters,
a few of which are listed in Table 38. Chemically resistant esters

TABLE 38

ESTERS THAT CAN BE DETERMINED BY THE HYDROXAMIC ACID
COLORIMETRIC METHOD

Aliphatic	Aromatic
n-Amyl acetate	Benzyl benzoate
n-Butyl acetate	n-Butyl benzoate
γ-Butyrolactone	Dimethyl isophthalate
Dimethyl malonate	Dimethyl phthalate
Ethyl acetate	Dimethyl terephthalate
Ethyl formate	Methyl benzoate
Ethyl propionate	Methyl p-toluate
Methyl n-butyrate	
Methyl oleate	

10*

cannot be determined satisfactorily by the method because the reaction conditions are not strenuous enough.

The ferric hydroxamates of aliphatic esters absorb in the vicinity of 530 mμ while the aromatic derivatives absorb in the region of 550 to 560 mμ. Esters of dicarboxylic acids give colors essentially twice as intense as the corresponding monocarboxylic esters.

Acids, most amides, and nitriles do not interfere in the method. The reaction conditions are such that the latter two classes of compounds do not react. However, interference may be obtained from the more reactive species of amides. Acid chlorides and anhydrides react and can be determined by the method. Aldehydes and ketones interfere by depletion of the reagent; however, this interference can be minimized by increasing the hydroxylamine concentration. High concentrations of water decrease the sensitivity of the method, otherwise no difficulty will be experienced if the same water concentration is used in preparing the calibration curve. Certain transition metals, such as copper and nickel, interfere by forming complexes with the hydroxamic acids. Ions that form strong complexes with ferric ion interfere by decreasing the color intensity.

SUMMARY

The conventional aqueous potassium hydroxide method for the saponification of esters is satisfactory for all but the more chemically resistant and water insoluble esters, particularly, when a co-solvent is employed. Interference in this method from aldehydes and ketones can be eliminated by incorporating phenylhydrazine in the saponification medium. In this way, these carbonyl compounds are converted to the corresponding phenylhydrazones which are resistant to strong bases. This technique can also be used to determine vinyl esters. The acetaldehyde formed by saponification is converted to the phenylhydrazone and further consumption of base is obviated.

A saponification medium consisting of potassium hydroxide in diethylene glycol can be used to determine the more chemically resistant and water insoluble esters. A very high reaction temperature (b.p. of diethylene glycol is 245°C) is obtained under reflux conditions, thus, most esters will saponify quantitatively.

For the determination of low (0.05 to 1%) concentrations of esters the hydroxamic acid colorimetric method should be used. This procedure is applicable to most esters and is relatively free of interference.

REFERENCES

1. FLETCHER, J. P., JOHSON, J. B., unpublished data, Union Carbide Chemicals Company, South Charleston, W. Va.
2. GODDU, R. F., LE BLANC, N. F., WRIGHT, C. M., *Anal. Chem.*, 27, 1251 (1955).
3. KOETTSTORFER, J., *Z. Anal. Chem.*, 18, 199, 431 (1879).
4. SHAEFER, W. E., BALLING, W. J., *Anal. Chem.*, 23, 1126 (1951).

CHAPTER 9

CARBOXYLIC ACID ANHYDRIDES

THE anhydrides of carboxylic acids are normally quite reactive; therefore, they can be determined readily, usually by reaction with a compound containing an active hydrogen group. Anhydrides can be hydrolyzed to the parent acids and determined; however, most of these compounds contain free acids which would be included in the analysis. Because of this, methods for anhydrides must be specific for determining the anhydride in the presence of the corresponding acid.

One or another of the four methods presented in this chapter will apply to most problems encountered with anhydride analyses. Three of these methods are based upon the reaction of the anhydride with an amine to form the corresponding amide, and are designed principally for determining macro concentrations. The other method is based upon the formation of the hydroxamic acid which is determined colorimetrically. This method is used for low concentrations.

ANILINE-SODIUM HYDROXIDE METHOD

Aniline reacts with most anhydrides to form one equivalent of carboxylic acid and one equivalent of amide:

$$C_6H_5NH_2 + (R-\overset{\overset{O}{\|}}{C}-)_2O \longrightarrow R-\overset{\overset{O}{\|}}{C}-NHC_6H_5 + R-\overset{\overset{O}{\|}}{C}OH$$

The carboxylic acid formed in the above reaction, and any free acid originally present in the anhydride, can be determined by titration with standard sodium hydroxide using phenolphthalein indicator. Since most anhydrides contain some free acidity a correction for this must be made. Two equivalents of acidity from the

[150]

anhydride and the free acidity are determined by titration with standard sodium hydroxide, in the presence of pyridine, using phenolphthalein indicator. Pyridine functions as a catalyst for the reaction with sodium hydroxide and in its presence the reaction is practically instantaneous[5].

The difference between the total acidity obtained by direct titration in the presence of pyridine and the acidity after the aniline reaction, is a measure of the anhydride content of the sample. The method described here is a combination of the method of Radcliffe and Mendofski[4] and the method of Smith and Bryant[5].

Reagents. Pyridine, freshly distilled. This material should contain less than 0.02 m-equiv. per g primary and secondary amine as determined by the carbon disulfide method in Chapter 3.

Aniline, freshly distilled.

Standard 0.5 N sodium hydroxide.

Phenolphthalein indicator, 1% solution in pyridine.

Procedure: Aniline Reaction. Add 75 ml. of redistilled pyridine to each of two 250-ml. glass-stoppered Erlenmeyer flasks. Reserve one of the flasks as a blank. Weigh no more than 15 m-equiv. of anhydride plus free acid into the other flask. Effect complete solution of the sample and then add 20 ml. of aniline to each flask. Allow 15 min reaction time at room temperature. Add 25 ml. of water to each flask and titrate with standard 0.5 N sodium hydroxide using phenolphthalein indicator.

Total acidity. Add 50 ml. of water and 50 ml. of redistilled pyridine to each of two 250-ml. glass-stoppered Erlenmeyer flasks. Reserve one of the flasks as a blank. Weigh no more than 15 m-equiv. of anhydride plus free acid into the other flask. Effect complete solution. Heating may be required for the solution of maleic anhydride. With solid anhydrides, other than maleic, weigh the anhydride into a dry flask, dissolve in 20 ml. of pyridine, and then slowly add 50 ml. of distilled water. Titrate with standard 0.5 N sodium hydroxide using phenolphthalein indicator.

Calculation. The difference between the total acidity and the acidity from the aniline reaction is a measure of the anhydride content. The difference between twice the titration in the aniline reaction and the direct titration is a measure of free acidity.

Scope and Limitations. This method appears to be applicable to most carboxylic acid anhydrides. A few of the anhydrides that have been determined by the method are: acetic, butyric, endomethylenetetrahydrophthalic, maleic, phthalic, propionic, and tetrahydrophthalic anhydride. The method is not applicable to halogen substituted anhydrides, such as chloroacetic anhydride, because of side reactions to form the hydrogen halides. The method is particularly valuable for determining the purity of refined anhydrides and a precision of $\pm 0.2\%$ can be obtained for this application. The method is not readily adaptable to the determination of low concentrations of anhydride in the presence of large amounts of acid, because the anhydride is obtained by difference.

MORPHOLINE METHOD

Morpholine reacts with anhydrides to form amides and the corresponding carboxylic acid:

$$
\text{O} \quad \text{S} \quad \text{NH} + (R-\overset{\overset{\text{O}}{\|}}{C}-)_2\text{O} \longrightarrow \text{O} \quad \text{S} \quad N-\overset{\overset{\text{O}}{\|}}{C}-R + R-\overset{\overset{\text{O}}{\|}}{C}\text{OH}
$$

This principle is used in the method of Johnson and Funk[3] as the basis of one of the most versatile methods available for anhydrides.

In this method a measured excess of morpholine is reacted with the anhydride in methanol medium. The amount of morpholine consumed is determined by titration with standard methanolic hydrochloric acid, using a screened methyl yellow indicator. Under the conditions of the titration most carboxylic acids and the amides from morpholine are neutral and do not interfere.

Reagents. Approximately 0.5 N morpholine in methanol.

Standard 0.5 N methanolic hydrochloric acid. Standardize against tris (hydroxymethyl) aminomethane (Fisher's Certified Reagent) in water using bromocresol green indicator.

Methyl yellow-methylene blue mixed indicator. Dissolve 1.0 g of methyl yellow (p-dimethylaminoazobenzene) and 0.1 g of methylene blue in 125 ml. of methanol.

Procedure. Pipet 50.0 ml. of the 0.5 N morpholine reagent into each of two 250-ml. glass-stoppered Erlenmeyer flasks. Reserve one of the flasks as a blank. Weigh no more than 20 m-equiv. of anhydride into the other flask. React for 5 min at room temperature. (2-Ethylhexanoic anhydride requires 30 min.) Add 4 to 5 drops of the mixed indicator to each flask and titrate with the standard 0.5 N methanolic hydrochloric acid to the disappearance of the green color.

Scope and Limitations. This method has been successfully applied to the following anhydrides: acetic, butyric, 2-ethylhexanoic, glutaric, phthalic, propionic, and succinic. The method should be applicable to most carboxylic anhydrides, except for those that are derived from the stronger organic acids such as maleic and citraconic. In these cases, the acid formed by reaction with morpholine is sufficiently acidic to interfere with the indicator end point. Potentiometric titrations can be used to obviate this difficulty.

While this method is valuable for the analysis of high purity samples, it can be used equally well for low concentrations (0.01%) of anhydrides in the presence of the corresponding acids. In this application 0.02 N morpholine, 0.1 N methanolic hydrochloric acid, and sample sizes up to 10 g are recommended. In the presence of acids stronger than acetic, the sensitivity suffers because of the adverse affect of large amounts of these acids upon the end point.

The only known interferences, in this method, are compounds that react with morpholine to destroy its basicity. Such compounds are ketene, diketene, acid chlorides, isocyanates, and isothiocyanates. This method can be modified to determine most of these compounds quantitatively. Substances that are not neutral to the indicator under the conditions of the titration, such as mineral acids and tertiary amines, will of course interfere unless corrected for.

MORPHOLINE-CARBON DISULFIDE METHOD

The reaction of anhydrides with morpholine has been used as the basis of a simple method for the analysis of mixtures of anhydrides and acids[1]. In this method, the anhydride is reacted with a measured excess of morpholine in acetonitrile. The free acid in the sample and the acid formed by reaction of the anhydride are titrated with standard sodium hydroxide using thymolphthalein indicator. The addition of carbon disulfide at the equivalence point of this titration converts the excess morpholine to the corresponding dithiocarbamic acid (see Chapter 3). This acid is then titrated with the standard sodium hydroxide. The difference between a blank and a sample for the second titration is a measure of the anhydride. The difference between the two titrations is a measure of the free acid.

Reagents. Carbon disulfide, reagent grade.
2-propanol 99%.
Morpholine, approx. 0.2 N in acetonitrile.
Standard 0.1 N sodium hydroxide.
Thymolphthalein indicator, 1.0% pyridine solution.

Procedure. Pipet 25.0 ml. of the 0.2 N morpholine solution into each of two glass-stoppered Erlenmeyer flasks. Reserve one of the flasks as a blank. Weigh no more than 3.5 m-equiv. of acid and anhydride into the other flask. React at room temperature for 15 min. Add 75 ml. of 2-propanol and 5 to 6 drops of the thymolphthalein indicator to each flask. Titrate with the standard 0.1 N sodium hydroxide just to the indicator end point. Do not over-titrate. Record the volume of titrant and zero the buret. Add 20 ml. of water to the blank. Add 5 ml. of carbon disulfide to each flask. Titrate with standard 0.1 N sodium hydroxide to a blue or blue-green end-point stable for at least one min. The difference between the blank and the sample for the second titration is a measure of anhydride. The difference between the first titration and the second is a measure of free acid.

Scope and Limitations. This method has been applied to acetic, butyric, endomethylenetetrahydrophthalic, 2-ethylhexanoic, maleic methylglutaric, phthalic, propionic, and succinic anhydrides. The method is not applicable to acrylic anhydride, because morpholine adds across the unsaturation to form a tertiary amine. Chloro-acetic anhydride cannot be analyzed by the method because of a side reaction with morpholine to form hydrogen chloride. In addition to its versatility, this method is particularly useful for analyzing mixtures of anhydrides and acids, because both of these determinations can be obtained using a single weighed sample and a single titrant. The method is not as useful as the previously presented morpholine method for determining low concentrations of anhydrides in the presence of the corresponding acids.

The method is subject to the same interferences as the morpholine method of Johnson and Funk[3] except organic acids interfere quantitatively and tertiary amines are not basic to the indicator.

HYDROXAMIC ACID COLORIMETRIC METHOD

Anhydrides react with hydroxylamine according to the following equation:

$$(R-\overset{\overset{O}{\|}}{C}-)_2O + H_2NOH \longrightarrow R-\overset{\overset{O}{\|}}{C}-NHOH + R\overset{\overset{O}{\|}}{C}OH$$

The hydroxamic acids formed in this reaction react with ferric ion to form red colored complexes:

$$R-\overset{\overset{O}{\|}}{C}-NHOH + 1/n\ Fe^{+3} \longrightarrow \begin{array}{c} R-C-NH \\ \| \quad \| \\ O \quad O \\ \diagdown \quad \diagup \\ Fe/n \end{array}$$

This principle has been used as a basis for a colorimetric method for anhydrides by Goddu, LeBlac, and Wright[2]. Although other compounds such as esters and amides can be determined by similar procedures, the following method employs neutral hydroxylamine which ordinarily does not react with these compounds.

Reagents. Sodium hydroxide, 12.5 wt./vol. % in methanol.

Hydroxylamine hydrochloride, 12.5 wt./vol. % in methanol.

Neutral hydroxylamine. Neutralize a portion of the 12.5% hydroxylamine hydrochloride with the 12.5% sodium hydroxide using phenolphthalein indicator. Filter the solution through No. 42 Whatman filter paper. The reagent is stable for 4 hours.

Ferric perchlorate, 5 wt./vol. % in ethanol. Dissolve 5 g of ferric perchlorate (G. F. Smith Chemical Co.) in 10 ml. of 70 to 72% perchloric acid and 10 ml. of water. Dilute to 100 ml. with ethanol. Cool during the dilution to prevent excessive heating.

Ferric perchlorate, 0.0057 M. Pipet 40 ml. of the 5% ferric perchlorate into a 1000 ml. volumetric flask. Add 12 ml. of 70 to 72% perchloric acid and dilute to volume with anhydrous ethanol. Add the ethanol slowly and cool during the dilution.

Benzene, anhydrous. Dry over anhydrous calcium sulfate for 24 hours.

Procedure. Pipet 5 ml. of a benzene solution of the anhydride, containing 0.01 to 0.001 moles of anhydride, into a 25 ml. Erlenmeyer flask with a 19 × 22 ground glass joint. Pipet 5 ml. of the anhydrous benzene into another flask to be used as a blank. Pipet 3 ml. of the neutral hydroxylamine reagent into each flask. Add a boiling stone to each flask and attach water-cooled reflux condensers to them. Reflux the solutions for 10 min and cool to room temperature. Wash the contents of the flasks into 50-ml. volumetric flasks with the 0.0057 M ferric perchlorate reagent. Dilute to volume with the reagent. Allow the flasks to stand for 10 minutes then determine the absorbance of the sample, using 1 cm cells, vs. the blank at the wavelength of maximum absorbance (approx. 530 mμ). Determine the concentration of anhydride by reference to a calibration curve prepared from the anhydride being determined.

Scope and Limitations. This method has been applied to only a few anhydrides, e.g., acetic and toluic anhydrides; however, the method should be applicable to most compounds containing this functional group. The method is particularly valuable for determining low concentrations (0.05 to 0.1%) of anhydrides in non-interfering solvents. Although the morpholine method previously described can also be used for determination in this concentration range, much larger sample sizes are required.

The method is subject to interference from acid chlorides, lactones, and easily hydrolyzed esters such as formates, phenolic esters, peroxyesters, and esters of α-halogen substituted acids. Aldehydes and ketones will interfere by depletion of the reagent; however, this can be inhibited by increasing the hydroxylamine concentration. Salts of the transition metals may interfere by forming complexes with the hydroxamic acids. Certain substances that complex ferric ion, such as tartaric acid, may also interfere.

Carboxylic acids, amides, most esters, and nitriles do not interfere under the conditions of the method.

SUMMARY

The aniline-sodium hydroxide method for anhydrides is valuable for analyzing samples containing macro concentrations of anhydride. The method is not adaptable to the determination of low concentrations of anhydride in the presence of the corresponding acids, because the anhydride concentration is obtained by difference. The morpholine method is ideally suited for such determinations since carboxylic acids do not interfere. The morpholine-carbon disulfide method is applicable to most anhydrides, and can be conveniently used for analyzing mixtures of acids and anhydrides because both determinations are obtained on a single weighed sample and a single titrant is used. The colorimetric hydroxamic acid method is valuable for determining low (0.05 to 1.0%) concentrations of anhydrides in non-interfering solvents.

REFERENCES

1. CRITCHFIELD, F. E., JOHNSON, J. B., Anal. Chem., 28, 430 (1956).
2. GODDU, R. F., LeBLANC, N. F., WRIGHT, C. M., Anal. Chem. 27, 1251 (1955).
3. JOHNSON, J. B., FUNK, G. L., Anal. Chem. 1464 (1955).
4. RADCLIFFE, L. G., MENDOFSKI, S., J. Soc. Chem. Ind., 36, 628 (1917).
5. SMITH, D. M., BRYANT, W. M. D., J. Amer. Chem. Soc., 58, 2452 (1936).

CHAPTER 10

PEROXIDES

ORGANIC peroxides are oxidizing agents and can, therefore, be reduced. The ease with which reduction occurs depends upon the type of peroxide. Some are reduced readily while others are quite inert. The most common types, listed roughly in order of decreasing reactivity, are as follows:

Peroxide	Structure
Peracids	$\overset{\text{O}}{\overset{\|}{\text{RCOOH}}}$
Hydroperoxides	RCH_2OOH
Peresters	$\overset{\text{O}}{\overset{\|}{\text{RCOOR}}}$
Diacyl peroxides	$\overset{\text{O}\quad\text{O}}{\overset{\|\quad\|}{\text{RCOOCR}}}$
Dialkyl peroxides	RCH_2OOCH_2R

Of these types, the dialkyl peroxides are the most difficult to determine with ordinary reducing agents.

With one exception, the methods described in this chapter are based upon the reduction of peroxides with iodide ion:

$$\overset{\text{O}\quad\text{O}}{\overset{\|\quad\|}{\text{RCOOCR}}} + 2I^- \longrightarrow 2R\overset{\text{O}}{\overset{\|}{\text{C}}}O^- + I_2$$

Iodine formed in the reaction is determined volumetrically for macro concentrations and colorimetrically for low concentrations. The one exception mentioned above is a method based upon the direct titration with ceric ammonium sulfate.

[158]

SODIUM IODIDE-ACETIC ANHYDRIDE METHOD

Most peroxides react rapidly and completely with sodium iodide in acetic anhydride at room temperature. After the reaction is complete, water is added and the liberated iodine is titrated with standard sodium thiosulfate using starch indicator. The method described here is a modification of the procedure of Nozaki[3].

Reagents. Acetic anhydride, 99%.
Sodium iodide, reagent grade.
Standard, 0,1 N sodium thiosulfate.
Starch, 1% solution.

Procedure. Add 10 ml. of acetic anhydride to each of two heat-resistant pressure bottles. Add approximately 2 g of sodium iodide to each bottle and dissolve. Purge the bottles with nitrogen and weigh not more than 2.5 m-equiv. of peroxide into one of the bottles. Reserve the other bottle for a blank determination. Cap the bottles and allow them to stand for 20 min at room temperature. Cool the contents of the bottles slightly with tap water and uncap the bottles. Wash down the inside walls of each bottle with 100 ml. of distilled water and swirl carefully to effect hydrolysis of the anhydride. Titrate with the standard 0.1 N sodium thiosulfate to a light brown color. Add 5 ml. of the starch indicator and continue the titration to the disappearance of the blue color.

Scope and Limitations. The sodium iodide in acetic anhydride method has been applied to the determination of hydrogen peroxide, diacetyl peroxide, dibenzoyl peroxide, dilauroyl peroxide, and peracetic acid. The method appears to be applicable to most peroxides, with the exception of the chemically resistant types such as the dialkyl peroxides. In fact the method can be used to determine the more reactive peroxides in the presence of certain dialkyl peroxides.

Although air oxidation does occur with the reagent, this problem is not as serious in acetic anhydride medium as in other media that have been used for peroxide determinations. Interference from unsaturated compounds is also minimized in acetic anhydride medium because of the anhydrous conditions used.

Inorganic ions that are reduced by sodium iodide under the conditions of the method will interfere. Such interferences are minimized because of the absence of water in the system.

HYDROGEN IODIDE–ACETIC ACID METHOD

Although the dialkyl peroxides can not be determined using conventional iodide reduction methods, these resistant peroxides can be reduced with constant boiling (56 per cent) hydrogen iodide in acetic acid medium:

$$RCH_2OOCH_2R + 2HI \longrightarrow 2RCH_2OH + I_2$$

The following method, which is a modification of the method of Dickey and co-workers [1], is the only iodometric method that has been applied successfully to dialkyl peroxides.

> *Reagents.* Acetic acid, glacial,
> Hydrogen iodide, constant boiling, iodine free. Distill 55 to 58% hydrogen iodide over red phosphorus in a carbon dioxide atmosphere. Reflux for several minutes then collect the reagent in a brown bottle. Discard the reagent when it becomes discolored.
> Distilled water, oxygen free. Prepare by saturating the water with carbon dioxide.
> Standard 0.1 N sodium thiosulfate.
> Starch indicator, 1% solution.

> *Procedure.* Add 10 ml. of glacial acetic acid to each of two heat-resistant pressure bottles. Purge the bottles with carbon dioxide for 5 min. Weigh not more than 2.5 m-equiv. of peroxide into one of the bottles, cap the bottles, and reserve the other bottle for a blank determination. Uncap the bottles separately and quickly add 5 ml. of the constant boiling hydrogen iodide to each. Recap the bottles using a piece of 1 mil Teflon film to protect the rubber gaskets. Insert the bottles in fabric bags and place them in a water bath at 60°C for 2 hr. Remove the bottles from the bath and cool them to room temperature. Remove the bags, uncap the bottles separately, add 150 ml. of oxygen-free water and titrate immediately with 0.1 N sodium thiosulfate. Add 2 ml. of starch indicator near the end point and continue the titration to the disappearance of the blue color.

Scope and Limitations. Because of the powerful reducing strength of the hydrogen iodide-acetic acid system, this method is applicable to the determination of di-*tert.*-butyl peroxide. The method should also be applicable to other dialkyl peroxides, since several other peroxides of this class are more readily reduced than is the di-*tert.*-butyl derivative. The method can be applied to the other types of peroxides; however, this is not recommended because of the strenuous conditions used.

Interference from atmospheric oxygen is a problem in this method and precautions must be taken to insure an oxygen-free atmosphere for the reaction. Interference can also be encountered from unsaturated compounds and compounds that can be reduced. For this reason the method should be used only for the more chemically resistant peroxides.

CERIC AMMONIUM SULFATE METHOD

Ceric ammonium sulfate has been used to differentiate between hydrogen peroxide and peracetic acid [2]. This oxidizing agent is reduced by hydrogen peroxide as follows:

$$2Ce^{+4} + H_2O_2 \longrightarrow 2Ce^{+3} + 2H^+ + O_2$$

The cerous ion formed is not a strong enough reducing agent to react with peracids, therefore, no interference is obtained from this type of peroxide. In the method described here, hydrogen peroxide is titrated directly with standard ceric ammonium sulfate using ferroin indicator.

Reagents. Sulfuric acid, 5%.
  Standard 0.1 N ceric ammonium sulfate in 5% sulfuric acid. Standardize as follows: Add 150 ml. of distilled water and 20 ml. of a 15% potassium iodide solution to an Erlenmeyer flask. Pipet 25.0 ml. of the ceric ammonium sulfate into the flasks and allow 15 min reaction time. Titrate with standard 0.1 N sodium thiosulfate using starch indicator.
  Ferroin indicator. Dissolve 1.458 g of o-phenanthroline and 0.695 g of ferrous sulfate heptahydrate in 100 ml. of distilled water.
Procedure. Add 150 ml. of 5% sulfuric acid to each of two 250-ml. glass-stoppered Erlenmeyer flasks. Cool the flasks to 0 to 10°C. Add sufficient cracked ice to maintain this temperature. Reserve one of the flasks as a blank. Weigh no more than 4 m-equiv. of hydrogen peroxide into the other flask. Add 3 drops of the ferroin indicator and titrate with the standard 0.1 N ceric ammonium sulfate just to the disappearance of the salmon-pink color.

Scope and Limitations. This method can be used to determine as little as 0.1 per cent hydrogen peroxide in 30 per cent peracetic acid. Hydroperoxides also react with the reagent and could possibly be determined selectively by the method. Diacyl and dialkyl peroxides do not react at the reduced temperatures used. Although the method has only been applied to hydrogen peroxide, the selectivity exhibited for hydroperoxides may be of value for other applications. Interferences in the method are limited to compounds that will reduce ceric ion or will oxidize cerous ion.

COLORIMETRIC SODIUM IODIDE–ACETIC ANHYDRIDE METHOD

The sensitivity of the sodium iodide-acetic anhydride method previously discussed can be increased significantly by measuring the iodine, formed in the reduction, colorimetrically. The following method which is designed for determining ppm concentrations of peroxides is based upon this principle. In the method the iodine formed is measured spectrophotometrically at 430 mμ.

Reagents. Acetic anhydride, 99%.
Sodium iodide, reagent grade.

Procedure. Add approximately 2 g of sodium iodide to each of two 125-ml. glass-stoppered Erlenmeyer flasks. Pipet 20 ml. of acetic anhydride into each flask and swirl the flasks to dissolve the sodium iodide. Purge each flask with nitrogen and keep the flasks stoppered except during the sample addition. Reserve one of the flasks as a blank. Add an amount of sample containing 3 to 15 μmoles of peroxide to the other flask. Add the same volume of acetic anhydride to the blank. Allow the flasks to stand at room temperature for 10±2 min. Determine the absorbance of the sample vs. the blank at 430 mμ using 1 cm spectrophotometric cells. Determine the concentration of peroxide from a calibration curve prepared using the peroxide being determined. If the pure peroxide is not available, obtain a calibration curve using hydrogen peroxide.

Scope and Limitations. This colorimetric modification of the sodium iodide-acetic anhydride method can be used to determine the same peroxides as mentioned in the discussion of the volumetric procedure. The method is ideally suited for determining ppm concentrations of peroxide in the presence of most organic materials. The method is subject to most of the same limitations as the volumetric procedure, and cannot be applied to dialkyl peroxides.

SUMMARY

The volumetric sodium iodide-acetic anhydride procedure can be applied to most types of peroxides with the exception of the dialkyl peroxides. The method is accurate and relatively free from interferences. Dialkyl peroxides can be determined by reduction with constant boiling hydrogen iodide (56 per cent) in acetic acid medium. Because of the great reducing power of the reagent, this method should be restricted to peroxides that cannot be determined by the sodium iodide-acetic anhydride method. Hydrogen peroxide, and possibly hydroperoxides, can be determined in the presence of other types of peroxides by direct titration with ceric ammonium sulfate. This method is of considerable value because of its selectivity. Parts per million concentrations of peroxides can be conveniently determined by a colorimetric modification of the sodium iodide-acetic anhydride method. The colorimetric method should be used when increased sensitivity is required.

REFERENCES

1. DICKEY, F. II., RALEY, J. H., RUST, F. F., TRESEDER, R. S., VAUGHAN, W. E., Ind. Eng. Chem., 41, 1673 (1949)
2. GREENSPAN, F. P., MacKELLAR, D. G., Anal. Chem., 20, 1061 (1948)
3. NOZAKI, K., Ind. Eng. Chem., Anal. Ed. 18, 583 (1946)

CHAPTER 11

SULFUR COMPOUNDS

SULFUR exists in organic compounds in a wide variety of functional groups. A few of the more common types of organic sulfur compounds are:

Type	Structure
Mercaptans	RSH
Sulfides	RSR'
Disulfides	RSSR'
Sulfates	RSO^{-4}
Sulfonates	RSO^{-3}

Mercaptans are fairly reactive compounds and several methods have been proposed for their determination. Such methods are usually based upon reaction of the active hydrogen of the -SH group or upon oxidation to the corresponding disulfide. Two methods that are fairly generally applicable are presented in this chapter. The first method is based upon the direct titration with mercuric ion, while the second is based upon the oxidation with iodine.

Sulfides and disulfides can be oxidized with bromine to form the corresponding sulfoxides and sulfonic acids, respectively. A method based upon the direct titration with potassium bromate is presented for determining these two classes of organic sulfur compounds.

The alkali metal alkyl sulfates are neutral salts and the corresponding acids (esters of sulfuric acid) are strongly acidic and can be titrated directly. The alkali metal alkyl sulfates, themselves, can be acid hydrolyzed to sodium hydrogen sulfate and a method based upon this principle is presented. The higher molecular weight sulfates and sulfonates are anionic surfactants and two methods based upon this principle are described. The volumetric

[164]

method is designed for macro concentrations of surfactants while the colorimetric method is designed for low concentrations.

TITRATION OF MERCAPTANS WITH MERCURIC PERCHLORATE

Mercaptans react with mercuric ion to form the corresponding non-dissociated mercaptides:

$$2RSH + Hg^{++} \longrightarrow (RS)_2Hg + 2H^+$$

This principle has been used by Fritz and Palmer [2] as the basis of a simple and accurate direct titration method for mercaptans. In this method, the mercaptan is dissolved in acetone and titrated with standard mercuric perchlorate using thio-Michler's ketone as the indicator.

Reagents. Mercuric perchlorate, 0.05 M; Dissolve approximately 26 g of mercuric perchlorate trihydrate (G. Frederick Smith Chemical Co.) in one liter of 0.1 M perchloric acid and filter. Standardize against 0.05 M EDTA at pH 6 (pyridine buffer) using thio-Michler's ketone indicator.

Thio-Michler's ketone; Dissolve 0.01 g of 4,4'-bis (dimethylamino) thiobenzophenone in 100 ml. of acetone. Prepare fresh indicator prior to use.

Procedure. Add 100 ml. of acetone to each of two 250-ml. glass-stoppered Erlenmeyer flasks. Reserve one of the flasks as a blank. Weigh not more than 0.6 to 2.0 millimoles of mercaptan into the other flasks. Add 1 ml. of pyridine and sufficient thio-Michler's ketone to each flask to make the solution a vivid yellow-green. Titrate with the standard 0.05 M mercuric perchlorate to a blue end point.

Scope and Limitations. Most primary, secondary, and tertiary mercaptans can be titrated satisfactorily with mercuric perchlorate and some compounds that have been determined in this manner are listed in Table 39 [2]. In the absence of interferences, the method is accurate to 0.2 per cent for the determination of refined mercaptans.

The method is relatively free from interference. Serious interference is encountered from only elemental sulfur, inorganic sulfides, iodides, cyanides, and thiocarbonyl compounds. Excessive amounts of acetonitrile (500:1 mole ratio) and styrene (25:1 mole ratio) will also interfere in a positive direction. The titration solution must be essentially neutral, otherwise erroneous results will be obtained. Neutralization should be conducted in water or ethanol media before the addition of the sample to acetone. In acetone medium, in the presence of strong acids, mercaptans are formed and these compounds will not titrate with mercuric ion.

TABLE 39

MERCAPTANS THAT CAN BE TITRATED DIRECTLY
WITH MERCURIC PERCHLORATE

2-Benzoxazolethiol	1-Octadecanethiol
p-tert-Butylthiophenol	1-Octanethiol
p-Chlorothiophenol	tert-Octyl mercaptan
1-Decanethiol	Isooctyl mercaptoacetate
Glycol dimercaptoacetate	Thionalide
Mercaptoacetic acid	α-Toluenethiol
2-Mercaptoethanol	Toluenethiol (mixed isomers)
3-Mercaptopropionic acid	Xylenethiol (mixed isomers)
Mercaptosuccinic acid	

IODOMETRIC METHOD FOR MERCAPTANS

Certain mercaptans are readily oxidized by iodine to the corresponding disulfides:

$$2RSH + I_2 \longrightarrow RSSR + 2HI$$

This principle has been used extensively for the determination of mercaptans. A few mercaptans can be titrated directly with iodine, however, a more generally applicable procedure involves the use of excess iodine and titration of the amount unconsumed in the reaction with standard sodium thiosulfate using starch indicator [4].

Reagents. Iodine, 0.1 N.
　　　　　Standard 0.1 N sodium thiosulfate.
　　　　　Starch indicator.

Procedure. Pipet 50.0 ml. of 0.1 N iodine into each of two 250-ml. glass-stoppered Erlenmeyer flasks. Reserve one of the flasks as a blank. Weigh not more than 3.0 m-equiv. of mercaptan into the other flask. Add sufficient ethanol to effect solution of the sample. Add the same volume of ethanol to the blank. Allow the flasks to stand for 15 minutes. Titrate with standard 0.1 N sodium thiosulfate using starch indicator near the end point.

Scope and Limitations. The iodometric method is applicable to most primary mercaptans, and is accurate and simple to use when it can be applied. Some secondary and tertiary mercaptans cannot be determined by the method, because the oxidation is either too slow or non-stoichiometric. These mercaptans can be determined more successfully by the mercuric perchlorate method.

Hydrogen sulfide will interfere in the method, as will any substance that can be oxidized by iodine. Unsaturated compounds that add iodine will, of course, also interfere.

POTASSIUM BROMATE METHOD FOR SULFIDES AND DISULFIDES

Organic sulfides react with bromine to form the corresponding sulfoxide:

$$RSR + Br_2 + H_2O \longrightarrow R_2SO + 2\,HBr$$

In the presence of excess bromine the sulfoxide is further oxidized slowly to the corresponding sulfone:

$$R_2SO + Br_2 + H_2O \longrightarrow R_2SO_2 + 2HBr$$

Organic disulfides also undergo similar oxidation with bromine:

$$RSSR + 5Br_2 + 6H_2O \longrightarrow 2RSO_3H + 10HBr$$

This principle is the basis of the method of Siggia and Edsberg for determining sulfides and disulfides [5]. In their method, the sulfur compounds are titrated directly with standard potassium bromate (generating the bromine *in situ*) to avoid an excess of bromine and oxidation of the sulfoxides to the sulfones.

Reagents. Standard 0.1 N potassium bromate. Dissolve 2.78 g of potassium bromate and 10 g of potassium bromide in one liter of water. Standardize against sodium thiosulfate in acidic media by converting the bromine to iodine with potassium iodide.

Procedure. Add 40 ml. of glacial acetic acid and 10 ml. of water to each of two 250-ml. glass-stoppered Erlenmeyer flasks. Reserve one of the flasks as a blank. Weigh not more than 3 millimoles of sulfide or 0.3 millimoles of disulfide into the other flask. Add 3 ml. (25 ml. for disulfides) of concentrated hydrochloric acid to each flask. Titrate with the standard 0.1 N potassium bromate until the bromine color persists. For disulfides, the titration should be conducted at 30 to 50°C to accelerate the rate of oxidation.

Scope and Limitations. This method has been applied to diethyl, di-n-butyl, diisobutyl, and dibenzyl sulfides and ethyl, n-butyl, and phenyl disulfides, and 1-cystine.

Mercaptans interfere in the method and can be corrected for by an independent determination, if the mercaptan content of the sample is less than 10 per cent. For samples containing more mercaptan than this, the error introduced is excessive since the bromine oxidation of mercaptans is somewhat non-stoichiometric.

Unsaturated compounds or other compounds that react with bromine will, of course, interfere. Such interferences are minimized, however, because only a slight excess of bromine is present at the end point.

ACID HYDROLYSIS OF ALKYL SULFATES

Salts of the mono-substituted alkyl esters of sulfuric acid can be hydrolyzed with hydrochloric acid to the corresponding alcohol and bisulfate ion:

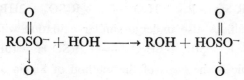

This principle has been used as the basis of a method for determining sodium alkyl sulfates which are important anionic surfactants[3]. In the following modification, the alkyl sulfate is hydrolyzed with hydrochloric acid, using dioxane as a co-solvent. The bisulfate ion formed is titrated with standard sodium hydroxide using alizarin red S-National fast acid green B mixed indicator.

Reagents. Dioxane, redistilled over potassium hydroxide pellets.
Butyl Carbitol.
Hydrochloric acid, 6% in dioxane. Add 150 ml. of concentrated hydrochloric acid to 250 ml. of distilled water and dilute to one liter with dioxane.

Standard 0.5 N sodium hydroxide.

Mixed indicator. Dissolve 0.5 g of alizarin red S and 0.14 g of National fast acid green B in 50 ml. of distilled water.

Procedure. Add 10 ml. of dioxane to each of two heat-resistant pressure bottles. Reserve one of the bottles as a blank. Weigh not more than 8 m-equiv. of alkyl sulfate into the other bottle. Add a few drops of mixed indicator to each bottle and neutralize the solutions with hydrochloric acid or sodium hydroxide whichever is required. Pipet 20.0 ml. of the 6% hydrochloric acid into each bottle. Cap the bottles, insert them in fabric bags, and place them in a steam bath at $98\pm2°C$ for 2 hours. Remove the bottles from the bath, cool to room temperature, uncap the bottles, and remove the bags. Add 100 ml. of butyl Carbitol to each bottle. Add more indicator if necessary and titrate with the standard 0.5 N sodium hydroxide to a bluish purple color.

Scope and Limitations. This method has been applied to the following sodium alkyl sulfates: 2-ethylhexyl, heptadecyl, lauryl, nonadecyl, and tetradecyl. The method has also been applied to triethanolammonium tetradecyl sulfate. Other salts of the mono-substituted alkyl esters of sulfuric acid can no doubt be determined, if the base from which the salt is derived has a pK_a greater than approximately 7.

Esters that are hydrolyzed with hydrochloric acid will interfere. Also, low molecular weight alcohols may interfere by forming alkyl chlorides under the conditions of the method.

TITRATION OF SURFACE ACTIVE SULFATES AND SULFONATES WITH CETYL PYRIDINIUM BROMIDE

The higher molecular weight ($>C_8$) alkyl sulfates and sulfonates are anionic surfactants and will combine with methylene blue to form complexes that are soluble in chloroform. Cationic surfactants such as cetyl pyridinium bromide will replace methylene blue in the complex causing the dye to migrate from the chloroform phase. This principle is the basis of a method developed by Epton [1] for the direct titration of surface active sulfates and sulfonates. In the method, the sample is added to a two-phase system of chloroform and an aqueous solution of methylene blue. The methylene blue then concentrates in the chloroform phase. The two-phase system is then titrated with standard cetyl pyridinium bromide until the color of both phases are equivalent.

Reagents. Methylene blue solution. Dissolve 0.05 g of methylene blue in one liter of distilled water. Add 10 ml. of concentrated sulfuric acid and 50 g of anhydrous sodium sulfate.

Standard cetyl pyridinium bromide, 0.005 M. Filter through No. 42 Whatman filter paper prior to use. Standardize against Aerosol OT, sodium dioctyl sulfosuccinate (American Cyanamid Co.) which has previously been assayed by saponification. Use the procedure described below for the standardization.

Procedure. Prepare an aqueous dilution of the sample so that a 10-ml aliquot will contain not more than 0.075 m-equiv. of anionic surfactant. Pipet 10.0 ml. of the dilution into a 100 ml. oil-sample bottle. Add 20 ml. of the methylene blue solution and 25 ml. of chloroform to the bottle. Stopper the bottle and shake vigorously for several seconds. Titrate with the standard cetyl pyridinium bromide until the blue color in the chloroform layer begins to migrate to the aqueous layer. Add the reagent in 1.0 ml. increments, shaking the bottle vigorously after each addition of titrant. Continue the titration by adding the reagent dropwise until the end point is reached. At this point the color intensity of both layers is identical.

Scope and Limitations. This method is applicable to most surface active alkyl sulfonates and sulfates. Sufficient surface activity to be determined by the method is not present in sulfonates and sulfates where the alkyl group contains less than eight carbon atoms. A few compounds that have been determined by the method are listed in Table 40.

TABLE 40

COMPOUNDS THAT CAN BE TITRATED WITH
CETYL PYRIDINIUM BROMIDE

Sodium 4-chloro-2-methylphenoxyethyl sulfate
Sodium 2,4-dichlorophenoxyethyl sulfate
Sodium 2-ethylhexenyl sulfonate[a]
Sodium 2-ethylhexyl sulfate
Sodium heptadecyl sulfate
Sodium lauryl sulfate
Sodium nonadecyl sulfate
Sodium tetradecyl sulfate
Triethanol ammonium tetradecyl sulfate

[a] 10 ml. of acetonitrile should be used to aid phase separation.

Large amounts of inorganic salts and low molecular weight sulfonates and sulfates interfere in the method by affecting the methylene blue migration. Outside of this problem, the method is relatively free from interferences.

COLORIMETRIC METHOD FOR SURFACE ACTIVE SULFATES AND SULFONATES

The reaction of methylene blue with surface active alkyl sulfates and sulfonates to form chloroform soluble complexes [1] can be used as the basis of a colorimetric method for these compounds. In the colorimetric method, the surface active compound is added to a two-phase system of chloroform and aqueous methylene blue. The colored complexes migrate to the chloroform layer and the amount of color in the layer is proportional to the surface active sulfate or sulfonate present.

Reagents. Chloroform, reagent grade. Wash with water immediately prior to use.

Methylene blue solution. Prepare in the same way as in the previous method.

Procedure. Add 50 ml. of water-washed chloroform and 50 ml. of methylene blue solution to each of two 250-ml. separatory funnels. Reserve one of the funnels as a blank. Add a volume of the aqueous sample containing 0.5 to 2 μmoles of anionic surfactant to the other funnel. Add an equal volume of water to the blank funnel. Stopper each funnel and shake the contents. Allow the funnels to stand at room temperature for 15 minutes. Determine the absorbance of the sample vs. the blank (chloroform layers) at 570 mμ using 1 cm spectrophotometric cells. Determine the amount of anionic surfactant from a calibration curve prepared from the pure compound if possible.

Scope and Limitations. This method is applicable to the same surface active alkyl sulfates and sulfonates as the previously described titrimetric method. However, the method is more sensitive and can be used to determine, readily, 10 ppm anionic surfactant in water using a 10-ml. sample. The method is subject to the same interferences as the titrimetric procedure.

REFERENCES

1. EPTON, S. R., *Trans. Faraday Soc.*, **44**, 226 (1948).
2. FRITZ, J. S., PALMER, T. A., *Anal. Chem.*, **33**, 98 (1961).
3. GRIMSHAW, A. H., *Textile World*, **79**, 1212 (1931).
4. KIMBALL, J. W., KRAMER, R. L., REID, E. E., *J. Am. Chem. Soc.*, **43**, 1199 (1921)
5. SIGGIA, S., EDSBERG, R. L., *Anal. Chem.*, **20**, 938 (1948).

SUBJECT INDEX

178   ORGANIC FUNCTIONAL GROUP ANALYSIS

184   ORGANIC FUNCTIONAL GROUP ANALYSIS